WEATHER ON THE PLANETS

George Ohring, who is director of the Meteorology Laboratory of the GCA Corporation, began his atmospheric studies at the City College of New York, and received Masters and Ph.D. degrees from New York University. Before his association with the GCA Corporation, he was atmospheric physicist with the Air Force Cambridge Research Center in Bedford, Massachusetts, and earlier, assistant meteorologist in the Department of Meteorology and Oceanography at New York University.

Dr. Ohring has contributed articles to the *Journal of the Atmospheric Sciences, Icarus,* and the *Bulletin of the American Meteorological Society.* He has been a participant in several international conferences, including the International Ozone Conference in Oxford, England, in 1959; the International Astrophysical Symposium in Liége, Belgium, in 1962; and the International Conference on Atmospheric Radiation in Leningrad, U.S.S.R., in 1964.

He wrote WEATHER ON THE PLANETS, he says, with the thought that "one of the young people reading the book quite possibly could be one of our first astronauts to land on Mars."

WEATHER
ON THE PLANETS

What We Know About Their Atmospheres

GEORGE OHRING

Published by Anchor Books
Doubleday & Company, Inc.
Garden City, New York
1966

Illustrations by Laura Shafran

The Science Study Series edition is the first
publication of *Weather on the Planets*.

LIBRARY OF CONGRESS CATALOG CARD NUMBER 66–17455
COPYRIGHT © 1966 BY EDUCATIONAL SERVICES
INCORPORATED
ALL RIGHTS RESERVED
PRINTED IN THE UNITED STATES OF AMERICA

THE SCIENCE STUDY SERIES

This book is one of a number that will appear in the Science Study Series through the collaboration of Educational Services Incorporated and the American Meteorological Society.

The Science Study Series was begun, in 1959, as a part of the Physical Science Study Committee's program to create a new physics course for American high schools. The Committee started its work in 1956, at the Massachusetts Institute of Technology, but subsequently became the nucleus of Educational Services Incorporated, of Watertown, Massachusetts, which has carried on the development of new curricula in several fields of education, both in the United States and abroad. The work in physics has had financial support from the National Science Foundation, the Ford Foundation, the Fund for the Advancement of Education, and the Alfred P. Sloan Foundation.

The purpose of the Series is to provide up-to-date, understandable, and authoritative reading in science for secondary school students and the lay public. The list of published and projected volumes covers many aspects of science and technology and also includes history and biography.

The Series is guided by a Board of Editors:
Bruce F. Kingsbury, Managing Editor
John H. Durston, General Editor
and Paul F. Brandwein, the Conservation Foundation, and Harcourt, Brace & World, Inc.; Samuel A. Goudsmit, Brookhaven National Laboratory; Philippe Le-Corbeiller, Harvard University; and Gerard Piel, *Scientific American*.

Selected Topics in the Atmospheric Sciences

The American Meteorological Society, with the objectives of disseminating knowledge of meteorology and advancing professional ideals, has sponsored a number of educational programs designed to stimulate interest in the atmospheric sciences. One such program, supported by the National Science Foundation, involves the development of a series of monographs for secondary school students and laymen, and since the intended audiences and the standards of excellence were similar, arrangements were made to include their volumes on meteorology in the Science Study Series.

This series within a series is guided by a Board of Editors consisting of James M. Austin, Massachusetts Institute of Technology; Richard A. Craig, Florida State University; Richard J. Reed, University of Washington; and Verne N. Rockcastle, Cornell University. The Society solicits manuscripts on various topics in the atmospheric sciences by distinguished scientists and educators.

CONTENTS

WEATHER ON THE PLANETS

Chapter I

INTRODUCTION

Mariner IV: Mission to Mars

At 9:22 on the morning of November 28, 1964, a rocket rose from a firing pad at Cape Kennedy, Florida, to launch an unmanned spaceship called Mariner IV (Plate I) on a journey to the planet Mars. The primary purpose of the flight was to obtain the first close-up views of the so-called "red planet." Mariner IV carried an automatic telescopic television device which was to take twenty-two* pictures as the spacecraft flew by Mars at a distance of 10,000 to 7000 miles. A number of other measurements were to be made, including one to determine the amount of the Martian atmosphere.

This undertaking of Earthbound man to obtain close-up pictures of another planet accepted some difficult problems. The 575-pound spaceship had to be launched from a platform (the Earth) that was itself moving around the Sun at 66,000 miles per hour, and it had to be aimed so precisely that it

* Actually, only twenty-one complete pictures, plus a fraction of the twenty-second, were received.

would intercept a planet (Mars) traveling 54,000 miles per hour, at a point in space some 250 million miles away. For a comparable degree of accuracy a baseball pitcher would have to throw a strike on a diamond on which his mound was five miles from home plate, and while both the pitcher's mound and home plate were moving at different speeds—and with the pitcher's mound rotating to boot!

Along the way to Mars, Mariner IV had to orient itself in space to keep its solar cell batteries facing the Sun and its electronic eye pointed at the star Canopus to permit proper radio transmission back to Earth. It had to receive, store, and execute radio commands from Earth. Near the planet the spaceship had to be so positioned that its television camera was pointed at the proper angle. And with only a very small power supply it had to radio its observations back to Earth over distances never before covered.

The television camera on Mariner IV was so designed that useful pictures could be obtained only if the spaceship passed within about 10,000 miles of the surface of Mars. Several days after the launching, tracking information revealed Mariner IV to be on a path that would miss Mars by some 150,000 miles. This distance was far outside the design limits of the television camera, and if the spacecraft had continued on this path, the scientific mission would have been a failure. But the Jet Propulsion Laboratory Control Center, in California, had anticipated the problem and was ready to make a mid-course maneuver, or change of velocity, to guide

Mariner to within the required distance of Mars. After comparison of the actual flight path with that charted for the planned near-miss, the Jet Propulsion Laboratory's electronic computers determined the velocity correction needed. On the morning of December 5, 1964, when the spaceship was more than a million miles away, commands were transmitted by radio to Mariner IV for the execution of this complicated mid-course maneuver. Mariner IV then proceeded to place itself in a proper position, after which a small rocket motor ignited and burned for 20.07 seconds, adding the necessary velocity increase of just 28 miles per hour to assure a near-miss of the planet Mars.

For the next seven months, Mariner IV sped along, at almost six miles per second, through the hostile conditions of the near vacuum of space, to the historic encounter with Mars. On July 14, 1965, the spacecraft was closing on its target (Fig. 1). Because of the small supply of power and the great distance to the Earth, instantaneous transmission of any pictures successfully taken would not be possible. The data from the camera system were to be stored on a tape recorder and then transmitted bit by bit to Earth after the entire picture-taking sequence had been completed. The tape recorder was to pause between pictures so that all twenty-two photographs could be captured on 330 feet of tape. It would take over eight hours to transmit each picture.

On encounter day, scientists at the Jet Propulsion Laboratory Control Center for Mariner IV were un-

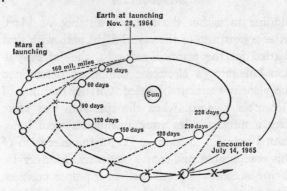

Fig. 1 The path of Mariner IV. The "x's" mark the successive positions of the satellite on the designated days as it traveled its curving course from the Earth's orbit to the intersection of the Mars orbit on July 14, 1965.

derstandably nervous. The television camera and tape recorder had not been tested for months. Had they survived the rigors of space? Would they work as planned? A radio signal was received from Mariner. It indicated that the tape was not stopping between pictures. This message could mean that not all the pictures would be recorded, that some might be erased, or, worst of all, that the tape recorder was completely out of order. Perhaps no picture at all would be transmitted back to Earth. All that night and into the morning of July 15, the scientists analyzed the trouble signal. By morning, to everybody's relief, they had satisfied themselves that the radio signal was a false one that had misled the computers. At 5:53 A.M. the first picture started to come in, and by the end of that day the entire first picture had been received. Ten days later, all twenty-two pictures had been transmitted and received on Earth. Seven and a half months after being launched into space, Mariner IV had successfully completed its spectacular mission to Mars.

What did Mariner find out? At this writing, the scientists are still analyzing the pictures and other data. Plate II is one of the photographs taken by Mariner. The Martian area it shows is about the size of the state of Massachusetts. The resolution of this picture is about thirty times better than can be obtained with the largest telescopes on Earth. Surface features as small as two miles wide can be seen, compared to the sixty-mile resolution of the best Earth-based telescopes. The outstanding characteristic revealed in this picture, as well as in others, is the presence of craters on the surface of Mars. They look like the craters of the Moon. No one had expected their presence in such number and size on Mars, and the discovery is one of the important results of the Mariner mission. We shall have more to say about these pictures in the chapter on Mars. From other measurements made by Mariner IV, scientists confirmed the belief that the atmosphere of Mars is thin, and they learned that Mars has no magnetic field.

The immense effort behind the voyage of Mariner IV to Mars is the late twentieth century's expression of a fascination that has existed for thousands of years. Almost from the beginning of recorded history the planets have aroused man's awe, superstition, sense of adventure, and curiosity. By no means the

least of these emotions has been his curiosity, re-
fined since the time of Galileo into a *scientific*
curiosity.

What are the planets like? Are they similar to
Earth? What is the composition of their atmospheres if they have atmospheres? What kinds of
weather have they? The list of questions scientists,
depending on their specialties, might ask about the
planets is endless, but these are illustrative of the
curiosity that will concern us mainly in this book.
We shall try to look at our neighbors of the solar
system through the eyes of the meteorologist.

The goal of research in meteorology is a thorough
understanding of what goes on in the Earth's atmosphere. The ultimate objective is the ability to
predict weather with high accuracy and well in ad-
vance, and possibly to change or "control" weather
and climate. In contrast to the experimental physicist, who can test his hypotheses under controlled
conditions in the laboratory, the meteorologist cannot perform controlled laboratory experiments. The
entire atmosphere is his laboratory, and to carry out
controlled experiments on such a scale is beyond his
powers. Nature, fortunately, affords another means
of getting at the problems. The other planets also
have atmospheres; their conditions are different
from those in the Earth's atmosphere. By studying
these atmospheres, with their own special conditions, we can learn more about planetary atmospheres in general and (we hope) our own in
particular. This new knowledge could result in bet-

ter weather forecasting, an important benefit for mankind.

There is a great deal of uncertainty concerning the origins of the planets and the entire life history of the solar system. Light may be thrown on these matters as we learn more about the present state of the planets. There is also the possibility of the present or past existence of some form of life on other planets in our solar system. Such a finding would be of profound significance to biologists and would help to clarify some of the theories concerning the origin and development of life on Earth, a subject of great uncertainty. As space exploration continues, unmanned and manned flights to the planets will certainly take place, and the atmospheric conditions will become an immediately practical concern. Knowledge of the environment of a planet is necessary for the design of spaceships and equipment to insure safe landings, proper operation of instruments, and safety of crews.

There are, as you can see, many excellent reasons for studying the planets. Nevertheless, planetary studies, although carried on more or less continuously since man first viewed these heavenly bodies, had been, until recently, the specialized field of a relatively small group of astronomers. However, as twentieth-century technology produces the means of space exploration, more and more scientists are beginning to study the planets. These scientists include researchers from the fields of meteorology, biology, geology, physics, and chemistry, as well as astronomers and astrophysicists. Some study planetary interiors and surfaces, some explore the possibilities of life on the planets, some theorize about the origin and life history of the planets, and some are interested in the atmospheres of the planets. It is the latter subject, the atmospheres of the planets, to which this book is devoted.

Are There Storms?

What would we like to know about the atmospheres of the planets? Many things. What is the composition of the gases that make up a planetary atmosphere? Are there clouds? If so, what do the clouds consist of? What are the temperatures? Is it windy? Is the air dry or humid? Are there storms? Are these storms rainstorms, snowstorms, dust storms, or some other kind of storms? What is the atmospheric pressure? What are the conditions in the upper atmosphere? How and why do other planets' atmospheres differ from the Earth's?

An enormous problem immediately confronts the scientist who wants to learn something about a planetary atmosphere. How do you learn something about an atmosphere millions of miles away? Even our closest planet, Venus, is at least 24 million miles from Earth. Pluto, the farthest distant, is at least 2700 million miles from us. If our scientist wants to determine the temperature of a planetary atmosphere he cannot, as on Earth, stick a thermometer into it. He can't take a sample of air and analyze it in the chemistry lab. He has no cosmic weather vane or anemometer for wind direction and speed. He must develop other observational techniques and apply theoretical reasoning to bridge these vast distances to the atmospheres of the other planets. In the next chapter we shall see how some basic principles of terrestrial science are applied to the task.

Chapter II

OBTAINING INFORMATION

Electromagnetic Radiation

All our observational information on planetary atmosphere is inferred from the radiation that the planets send us. Some of this radiation is visible—the sunlight that the planets and their atmospheres reflect back to space. Another part is invisible—the heat, for example, that the planets radiate. By suitable analysis of this radiation, scientists can deduce a great deal about planetary atmospheres.

Radiation consists of electromagnetic waves. The speed at which electromagnetic waves travel is very great—3×10^{10}* centimeters per second, or 186,000 miles per second. Sunlight travels from the Sun to the Earth, a trip of 93 million miles, in only 8.33 minutes. The distance between successive electromagnetic waves—that is, the distance between successive wave crests (Fig. 2) or wave troughs—is called the wavelength of the radiation. The number of wave crests or troughs that pass an observer in a

* For explanation of the symbols, units, and measurements used in this book see the Appendix.

*Fig. 2 Wavelength, designated by the Greek let-
ter lambda (λ), is the distance between successive wave crests. The term is applied to any form
of wave motion, including electromagnetic radiation.*

unit of time (customarily, one second) is called the
frequency of the radiation. A very simple relationship links wavelength, frequency, and the speed of
electromagnetic waves. In mathematical language
this relationship is written:

$$f\lambda = v = 3 \times 10^{10} \text{ centimeters per second}$$

where f is the frequency, λ the wavelength, and v
the speed of the waves. Translating this mathematical statement into words, we have the following:
the frequency multiplied by the wavelength equals
the speed of the waves, 3×10^{10} centimeters per
second.

All matter is capable of sending out, or emitting,
electromagnetic waves of various wavelengths. The
range of wavelengths that can be emitted by radiating bodies is enormous, as can be seen from Fig. 3.
This range is called the electromagnetic spectrum,
and the radiation in each portion of this spectrum
has been named. For example, the radiations with
very short wavelengths of about 10^{-8} cm ($3.94 \times
10^{-9}$ in.) are called X rays. These X rays are the
same X rays that a doctor uses in diagnosis. The

radiations with the very long wavelengths of 0.1 to 10^5 cm (3.94×10^{-2} in. to 3280 ft.) are called radio waves—the very same waves that make possible radio broadcasting. As you can see in Fig. 3, visible radiation, or light, occupies only a small portion of the entire spectrum. Human eyes see radiation in the portion of the spectrum whose wavelength varies from about 4×10^{-5} cm (1.57×10^{-5} in.) for violet light to about 8×10^{-5} cm (3.15×10^{-5} in.) for red light. White light is a mixture of all the radiations in this wavelength range. Human eyes cannot see any of the other electromagnetic waves.

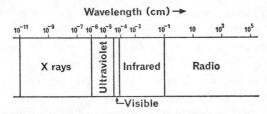

Fig. 3   The electromagnetic spectrum ranges from the longest radio waves to the very short X rays known as gamma rays. The diagram shows how narrow is the band of the visible region, the very small portion our eyes can see.

How then do we know they exist, and how can we measure them?

There is a characteristic technique for detecting waves from each portion of the spectrum. For example, the very long wavelength radiation can be detected with radio receivers. Infrared radiation is detected from its heating effect. X rays, ultraviolet radiation, and visible radiation can be measured through their chemical action on a photographic plate. We shall see in later chapters what these measurements tell us about a planet's weather and atmosphere.

Atmospheric Reduction of Electromagnetic Radiation

A beam of electromagnetic radiation—for example, a beam of sunlight—may be reduced upon passage through an atmosphere. Reduction can occur through any one of three processes: (1) absorption, (2) scattering, and (3) reflection.

In the Earth's atmosphere gases, such as water vapor (the gaseous form of water), carbon dioxide, and ozone, absorb radiation at certain wavelengths. Ozone strongly absorbs ultraviolet radiation; water vapor and carbon dioxide absorb radiation at many infrared wavelengths. Air molecules scatter radiation in all directions, thus reducing the intensity in the beam of radiation; such scattering is especially strong for short wavelength radiation. Dust particles and other atmospheric pollutants also absorb and scatter radiation. Reflection of radiation occurs at clouds. For example, clouds in the Earth's atmosphere reflect back to space much sunlight—cloudy days are dark. The net effect of these processes is to reduce the intensity of radiation, that is, the amount of energy striking a unit area of horizontal surface in one unit of time (for example, calories per cm² per second), as it passes through the atmosphere. Fig. 4 graphically summarizes the reductions of intensity. These same processes govern the transfer of radiation in all planetary atmospheres.

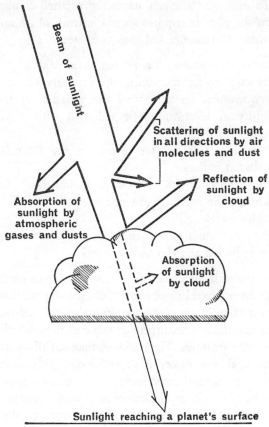

Fig. 4 *This diagram suggests how scattering and absorption in the atmosphere reduce the intensity of sunlight.*

While these processes help us in general to learn about a planetary atmosphere's characteristics, in some instances they hamper our search for knowledge.

To measure the electromagnetic radiation coming from the planets requires special instruments. Some of these instruments and their uses are:

Photographic plates   for making visual records
Photometers   for measuring the intensity of light
Spectrographs   for measuring the variation of the intensity of electromagnetic radiation with wavelength
Infrared radiometers   for measuring the intensity of infrared radiation
Radio telescopes (or *microwave radiometers*) for measuring the intensity of electromagnetic radiation at radio wavelengths
Radar   for sending out and receiving electromagnetic radiation at radio wavelengths

In the past all planetary observations were made from astronomical observatories. Even today most of our information on planetary atmospheres is derived from analysis of measurements made at these Earth-based observatories. The major component of an astronomical observatory is the telescope. Telescopes have two general functions: they magnify small objects, allowing resolution of a planet's features, and they gather a great deal of light, making dim planets brighter. Essentially, they allow us, or our instruments, to "see" better, or to see what the naked eye could not see at all. Telescopes are necessary because the planets and other heavenly bodies are so far away that they seem only bright points in the sky. The intensity of their light, which decreases as the square of the distance to the source, has been reduced considerably by the time it arrives at the Earth. Without the telescope* our light-measuring instruments would be useless for observing the planets and other heavenly bodies.

Suppose you had the job of selecting the location for a new astronomical observatory. What geographical features would you look for? Firstly, you would look for a region of minimum cloudiness; you would want to use your observatory the largest possible fraction of the time, and clouds, since they reflect much electromagnetic radiation, interfere with observations. Secondly, you would probably stay away from cities, which usually put large amounts of smoke and dust in their atmospheres and whose bright lights interfere with nighttime observations. Thirdly, you would seek a dry climate since water vapor, being an atmospheric gas that absorbs radiation in various parts of the electromagnetic spectrum, will filter the electromagnetic radiation you are trying to observe. Lastly, you might choose a mountaintop to get above as much of the Earth's atmosphere as possible; atmospheric gases, such as water vapor and carbon dioxide, and dusts deplete the electromagnetic radiation you are trying to meas-

---

* Any standard book on astronomy (see Suggested Additional Reading) will explain the working of telescopes. This book will not go into the technicalities.

ure. On the basis of these criteria you probably would build your observatory on a mountaintop, in the middle of a desert, far from any city or source of air pollution. (You might find it difficult to hire astronomers to work there—but that's another problem.)

Still, no matter where you place your observatory, atmospheric effects, mainly of two kinds, will hamper your observation. One effect, already discussed, is the absorption of electromagnetic radiation from the planets by gases and dusts in the Earth's atmosphere. Fig. 5 shows at what wavelengths gases in the Earth's atmosphere absorb radiation and at what wavelengths they are transparent to electromagnetic radiation. The other disturbing effect is atmospheric turbulence, which dis-

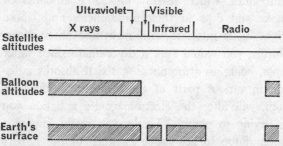

Fig. 5 A graphic representation according to altitude and wavelength of the atmospheric absorption of radiation. The horizontal bars indicate absorption. At the surface of the Earth all radiation except the visible and some infrared and radio wavelengths is absorbed. At balloon altitudes absorption in the infrared is absent. At satellite altitudes all radiation can be observed.

torts the light coming from the planets. A simple
example is the flickering, the so-called "heat waves,"
you see when you look out a window that is just
above a radiator. This effect blurs the image or picture and prevents land-based telescopes from per-
forming up to their theoretical specifications. The
only real solution would be to place astronomical
instruments above the Earth's atmosphere.

In recent years, plastic balloons have been developed that can lift heavy instruments as high as
twenty miles and float for several days before burst-
ing. At a height of twenty miles the balloon is above
99 per cent of the Earth's atmosphere; it has become a useful "platform" for planetary observation.
Instruments at these altitudes are able to observe,
with negligible atmospheric interference, the infrared spectrum from planets, for example. Absence
of turbulence makes it possible to realize the full
power of a telescope. The observatory is above bad
weather; longer observing periods are possible.
Measurements are either radioed immediately to
Earth or recorded on instruments, which are re-
covered after descending by parachute.

Earth satellites offer several advantages over balloons as platforms for observing the planets. While
balloon flights are limited to several days' duration,
satellites can remain in orbit for years. At balloon
altitudes oxygen and ozone in the small fraction of
atmosphere remaining above the balloon absorb
most of the planetary ultraviolet radiation. At satellite altitudes, which are above the Earth's atmosphere, ultraviolet radiation can be observed and

measured. Furthermore, a satellite telescope would be orbiting in the darkness of space above the Earth's atmosphere, and observations could be made during the day as well as the night, and the information transmitted to the Earth by radio. The launching of our first orbiting astronomical observatory is, at this writing, not far off.

Planetary probes are instruments for taking measurements of planetary characteristics in the vicinity of the planets rather than from the vicinity of the Earth. A spacecraft carries the instruments to a planet where the measurements are taken and radioed back to the Earth. The 1962 Venus fly-by of Mariner II was the first planetary probe.

The obvious advantage of a planetary probe is that it stretches the scientists' reach; their instruments can be placed close to, or even within, the atmosphere they are trying to learn something about. Thus, measurements of electromagnetic radiation can be made with much greater detail than is possible from the Earth. The most striking examples have been the wonderfully detailed television pictures of the Moon and Mars; the pictures showed much greater surface detail than had been obtained in centuries of Earth-based telescopic observations. Similarly, with observations in the ultraviolet, infrared, and radio wavelengths one could measure the detailed variations of these radiations over the surface of the planet, and also measure radiations too weak to be observed from the Earth.

As unmanned planetary probes are improved there will be opportunities for direct measurements of planetary characteristics from vehicles that enter the planet's atmosphere and land on its surface. Instead of drawing inferences from measurements of electromagnetic radiation, scientists will then be able to use such instruments as thermometers and barometers. They will measure directly atmospheric quantities that cannot be deduced at all from observations of electromagnetic radiation. Eventually man himself will make the journey and record his own observations of the planets.

Theoretical Techniques

To extend the information provided by direct observation, scientists apply theoretical techniques to derive the characteristics of a planetary atmosphere. The method in general can be described simply as the application of terrestrial logic, basic physics, and chemistry to the observational data to obtain a synthetic picture of what the given planetary atmosphere conceivably might be. Sometimes there is no basic principle that applies to a particular situation. In such cases scientists can do no better than make an educated guess. A hypothetical example will illustrate the method:

Suppose you were a scientist concerned with the chemical composition—the mixture of gases—of the atmosphere of neighboring planet X. The following facts are available to you from observations:

(1) The atmosphere of planet X has some carbon

dioxide in it, and this gas is the only one that has thus far been detected.

(2) The mass of planet X's atmosphere is much larger than the mass of the carbon dioxide in it.

(3) About 80 per cent of the Earth's atmosphere is nitrogen.

(4) Of the possible candidates among the gases nitrogen has a very high cosmic abundance—that is, large amounts of it are found in astronomical bodies, such as the Sun and the stars.

(5) It has not been possible to determine whether there is nitrogen in planet X's atmosphere (since nitrogen is difficult to detect spectroscopically from Earth-based observations).

You have the question, "What is your estimate of the composition of planet X's atmosphere?" If your answer is, mostly nitrogen with some carbon dioxide, you would be in agreement with your colleagues.

The answer would be based upon two arguments:

(1) Since the Earth's atmosphere is largely nitrogen, the atmosphere of neighboring planet X is probably largely nitrogen.

(2) Since nitrogen is abundant in most heavenly bodies, it is probably abundant in the atmosphere of planet X.

The two arguments may be called the terrestrial analogy and the cosmic abundance argument, respectively. The problem to which you have proposed a solution is not a fictitious one, since this is essentially the same problem that scientists have with the atmosphere of Venus, and their answer is that nitrogen is the major constituent of Venus' atmosphere. Whether or not this answer is correct will be determined only when a direct measurement of the nitrogen content is possible. In later chapters, we shall see other specific instances where theoretical reasoning helps us to solve problems.

Uncertainties

Observational and theoretical techniques are the "tools" used by scientists in acquiring information about planetary atmospheres. It should be pointed out, however, that there is a good deal of uncertainty in some of our derived information since our knowledge of planetary characteristics ranges all the way from an educated guess to a theoretical prediction that has been confirmed by an accurate observation. There are several sources from which these uncertainties arise, and we shall discuss them. We shall also illustrate how, in two specific instances, the supposed "facts" about a planet have changed.

Every observational technique has instrumental, or measurement, error associated with it. This error may be large or small, depending upon the particular technique and instrumentation. To the extent that error is present in an observation, it limits the accuracy and places a certain amount of uncertainty on the information derived from the observation.

In applying theoretical techniques one usually must make assumptions. When the assumptions are not completely valid, a theoretical prediction may be in error. Sometimes there are conflicting theories, and they, of course, may lead to different theoretical predictions, even from the same set of observational data and assumptions.

Probably the most important reason for the large uncertainties in our knowledge of the planets is the fact that our observational information is based not upon direct measurements within their atmospheres, but upon interpretation of remote observations of electromagnetic radiation received from the planets and their atmospheres. Our interpretations may be incorrect. For example, consider the photographs of other planets. Scientists who analyze the photographs must interpret them in terms of phenomena with which they are familiar, and the only familiar phenomena are those associated with the Earth and its atmosphere. Thus, a scientist doesn't hesitate to spot a cloud formation in a picture of another planet because from Earthly experience he knows what clouds look like. But there may be other atmospheric and surface phenomena that have no counterpart on the Earth. Pictures of the planets are extremely difficult to interpret.

Uncertainties decrease as improved observations and theoretical techniques and unambiguous interpretations become available. For example, a quite astonishing result in the field of planetary astronomy was the recent finding that the surface temperature of the planet Venus is remarkably high—about 800° F. This finding was based upon observations of the planet's emission of radio waves and was confirmed by the Mariner fly-by of Venus. Until these observations were made it was believed that the surface temperature of Venus was about the same or slightly higher than the temperature on the Earth. Now the problem is to explain why Venus has such a remarkably high temperature!

On very rare occasions scientists themselves do not realize the uncertainties associated with their observations. In 1895, one scientist estimated the rotation period of Venus—the time it takes to rotate once about its axis—to be 23 hours 57 minutes 36.2396 seconds. He later modified this to 23 hours 57 minutes 36.37728 seconds. The absurdity of these very "accurate" estimates—supposedly accurate to $\frac{1}{10,000}$ of a second—becomes apparent when one realizes that even today, with greatly improved measurement techniques, the uncertainty in the rotation period of Venus is about five days, not $\frac{1}{10,000}$ of a second. (The best observations available today indicate a period close to 250 days rather than 24 hours.)

The discussion of the limitations of our present knowledge and the examples of uncertainty should serve as a warning to the reader that some of the information about planetary atmospheres in the remainder of this book is tentative and subject to change. As we discuss in detail the atmospheres of the planets, we shall try to indicate the limits and uncertainties of our knowledge.

Chapter III

THE PLANETS:
THE BIG PICTURE

The solar system consists of the Sun and its family of planets. Including our own Earth, there are nine of these very large bodies of matter, and they revolve around the Sun, which is one of a vast number of stars. In increasing order of distance from the Sun the planets are Mercury, Venus, Earth, Mars, Jupiter, Saturn, Uranus, Neptune, and Pluto. If, to simplify the picture, we think of the Earth-Sun average distance as 1, then the average distances of the other planets to the Sun are as shown in Table 1. In actual miles this Earth-Sun average distance is about 93,000,000.

It is not very helpful to ask someone to visualize 93,000,000 miles. In Chapter I we used a baseball analogy to describe the Mariner IV mission, and here another baseball model might give more meaning to the comparative distances of the solar system. In Fig. 6 the relative positions of the planets are diagramed on a scale model of Yankee Stadium. Suppose the Sun to be home plate. (On this scale its size would be that of a ping-pong ball, while the Earth would be 100 times smaller.) Then Mercury,

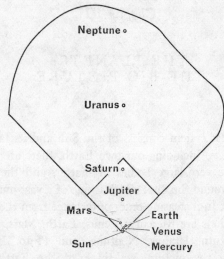

Fig. 6 *The solar system in a cosmic Yankee Stadium. With Jupiter pitching and the Sun at home plate, this is how the planets would take the field.*

Venus, Earth, and Mars would be within 20 feet of the plate, Jupiter at the pitcher's mound, Saturn near second base, Uranus in short center field, Neptune in deep center field, and Pluto in the center field bleachers.

The amount of the Sun's radiation (solar radiation) received by a planet decreases as the square of its distance from the Sun. You can convince yourself of the truth of this statement if you will visualize a light bulb in the center of a room. Now, imagine two spheres with centers at the light bulb, the first having a radius of one foot and the second a radius

of two feet (see Fig. 7). The surface area of a sphere
is given by

$$S = 4\pi r^2$$

where S is the surface area and r is the radius of the
sphere. The surface areas of our two imaginary
spheres are given by

$$S_1 = 4\pi(1)^2$$

and

$$S_2 = 4\pi(2)^2$$

The ratio of the areas, S_1/S_2, is ¼. Thus, the second sphere's surface area is four times the first's.

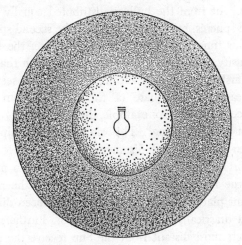

Fig. 7   *The shell of the outer sphere is twice as far
from the light as the inner sphere is and has four
times the area. The intensity of the light therefore
is spread over four times the area and at any spot
is one-fourth as great as on the inner shell.*

TABLE 1. PLANETARY CHARACTERISTICS

Planet	Average Distance from Sun (Earth = 1)	Solar Radiation Received (Earth = 1)	Orbital Period		Eccentricity	Equatorial Diameter (miles)
MERCURY	0.39	7	88	days	0.206	3,010
VENUS	0.72	2	225	days	0.007	7,620
EARTH	1.00	1	365	days	0.017	7,926
MARS	1.52	0.4	687	days	0.093	4,220
JUPITER	5.20	0.04	11.9	years	0.048	88,800
SATURN	9.54	0.01	29.5	years	0.056	74,000
URANUS	19.2	0.003	84.0	years	0.047	29,500
NEPTUNE	30.1	0.001	165	years	0.009	27,200
PLUTO	39.5	0.0006	248	years	0.249	3,600?

The light from the bulb is distributed equally over both spheres, but since the area of the second sphere is four times the area of the first sphere, the light intensity on the second sphere is one-fourth that on the first sphere. Thus, the light intensity is seen to decrease as the square of the distance from the source. At 10 feet, for example, the intensity is $\frac{1}{100}$ of what it is at 1 foot. This simple relationship between intensity and distance from the source has important ramifications. It is very difficult to measure the radiation emitted or reflected by the more distant planets, since this radiation has been diminished drastically on its trip to Earth. Further, the planets most distant from the Sun receive the least sunlight, and thus should be much colder than the planets closest to the Sun. The average amounts of solar radiation received by the planets are shown in

(NOTE: *Some of the planetary characteristics are presented in terms of the Earth's values for these characteristics. These cases are identified by the phrase Earth = 1*)

Mass (Earth = 1)	Gravity (Earth = 1)	Escape Velocity (mi./sec.)	Rotation Period	Inclination (Degrees)	Albedo
0.05	0.38	2.6	59 days	10?	0.06
0.81	0.89	6.4	250 days	6	0.73
1.00	1.00	6.95	23.9 hours	23.5	0.35
0.11	0.38	3.1	24.6 hours	25.2	0.30
317	2.64	37.7	9.9 hours	3.1	0.45
95	1.17	22.5	10.4 hours	26.7	0.50
14	1.03	13.6	10.8 hours	98	0.66
18	1.50	13.6	15.7 hours	29	0.62
?	?	?	6.4 days	?	0.15?

Table 1. You will see that the variation is considerable: Mercury receives seven times more solar radiation than the Earth does, while Pluto receives $\frac{6}{10,000}$ as much.

Of importance to the climates of planets are certain characteristics of their orbits, the paths on which they travel around the Sun. The planetary orbits are not quite circular but elliptical. The orbital period, or the time required to complete one revolution around the Sun, determines the length of the planetary year, which, in turn, determines the length of each season. The orbital period for each planet is listed in Table 1. It is evident from this table that the orbital period increases with increasing distance from the Sun. Mercury completes its trip around the Sun in only 59 days, compared to the Earth's 365 days, and Pluto's 248 years. The length of the Martian year is about twice the length of the Earth's year, and, hence, a season on Mars is about twice as long as a season on the Earth. The more distant planets can be expected to have still longer seasons.

The fact that planetary orbits are not circles but ellipses is important. It is quite simple to draw an ellipse. All you need are a couple of thumbtacks, some string, a pencil, and a piece of cardboard. Place the thumbtacks in the cardboard a small distance apart—say, about two inches. Tie the ends of the string together—a six-inch length will do rather nicely—and place it around the thumbtacks. Hold the pencil firmly against the piece of string to form a triangle with the two tacks. With the string tight, keep moving the pencil until it comes back to its starting point. You should now see a curve on the cardboard similar to the one sketched in Fig. 8. This is an ellipse. The two tacks are the foci of the ellipse. As the foci come closer together, the ellipse approaches a circle. The eccentricity of a planetary orbit is a measure of the departure of the orbit from a circle. The eccentricity of a circle is zero. Eccentricity is defined as the ratio of the distance between the foci to the major diameter of the ellipse traced out by the planetary orbit (see Fig. 7). The Sun is located at one of the foci of the ellipse.

Fig. 8 shows that a planet's distance from the Sun varies slightly in the course of the planetary year. The total amount of variation depends upon the eccentricity of the orbit. For planets with large orbital eccentricities, this variation can cause significant differences in the amount of solar radiation received and, hence, differences in average temperatures. With an eccentricity of only 0.017 the Earth's orbit is nearly circular, and this effect is negligible. But

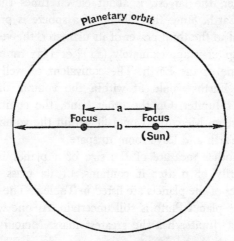

Fig. 8   The eccentricity of an elliptic planetary orbit is the distance a divided by the distance b.

in the case of Mars, whose orbit has an eccentricity of 0.093, there is probably a difference in average temperature between the time it is closest to and the time it is farthest from the Sun. Eccentricities of all the planetary orbits are listed in Table 1.

Sizes

The planets are approximately spherical in shape and a good measure of their sizes is their diameters.

These are listed in Table 1 and shown graphically in Fig. 9. The variation in size is considerable. Mercury, the smallest planet, has a diameter about 0.39 of the Earth's diameter, whereas the diameter of Jupiter, the largest, is about eleven times that of the Earth. Since the volume of a sphere is proportional to the third power of its diameter, the volume of Jupiter is approximately $(11)^3$ or 1331 times the volume of the Earth. The equivalent of well over 1000 Earths would fit within the volume of the planet Jupiter. On the other hand, the equivalent of sixteen Mercuries would fit within the volume of the Earth and leave room to spare.

Another measure of the size of a planet is the quantity of matter it contains, or its mass. The masses of the planets are listed in Table 1. The mass of the planet Pluto is still uncertain. As one would expect, Jupiter has the greatest mass, Mercury the smallest.

The mass of a planet is important since it is the mass that determines the planet's gravitational force; in fact, the force of gravity of any body, be it planet or something else, is directly proportional to the mass. On Earth you recognize the force of gravity in its effect on thrown balls and stones, but its influence extends far beyond the range of your senses. Strange as it may at first seem, the composition of the Earth's atmosphere, and of the other planetary atmospheres, is related to the strength of the gravitational forces.

Associated with each planet is a quantity called the escape velocity, which in this age of rockets and

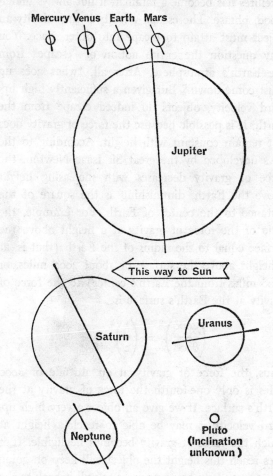

Fig. 9 *The relative sizes and inclinations of the planets.*

satellites has become a familiar, if not always under-
stood, phrase. The escape velocity is the velocity an
object must attain to escape into outer space. You
may question the entire notion of "escape" from
the Earth's atmosphere. After all, "what goes up
must come down." But given a sufficiently high upward velocity, objects do indeed escape from the
Earth. It is possible because the force of gravity does
not remain constant with height. According to the
laws developed by the great Sir Isaac Newton, the
force of gravity decreases with increasing height
above the Earth, diminishing as the square of the
distance to the center of Earth. For example, the
ratio of the force of gravity at a height above the
surface equal to the radius of the Earth (that is, at
a height above the surface of about 4000 miles, or
8000 miles from the Earth's center) to the force of
gravity at the Earth's surface is

$$\left(\frac{4000}{8000}\right)^2 = \left(\frac{1}{2}\right)^2 = \frac{1}{4}$$

Thus, the force of gravity at an altitude of 4000
miles is only one-fourth the force of gravity at the
Earth's surface. If we give an object a very high upward velocity it may be able to reach a height at
which the force of gravity becomes negligible. If it
does reach this height the object will keep on going
into space, there being no force to pull it back to the
Earth. Calculations reveal that the required initial
velocity—the escape velocity—for the Earth is about
7 miles/second. Since the escape velocity of a partic-

ular planet depends directly upon its force of gravity, we can expect planets with large gravitational forces to have high escape velocities and planets with small gravitational forces to have low escape velocities.

Now, what has all this to do with the composition of a planet's atmosphere? The gas molecules in the atmosphere of a planet are constantly in motion, and the lighter gases, such as hydrogen and helium, have higher average velocities than heavier gases, carbon dioxide for example. Over a long period of time a planet with a low escape velocity may lose most of the lighter molecules in its atmosphere. Conversely, a planet with a high escape velocity is likely to retain the lighter molecules in its atmosphere. Planets with extremely low escape velocities, such as Mercury, will have difficulty in retaining any atmosphere at all. One would expect such planets to have very small amounts of atmosphere with small atmospheric pressures. The force of gravity and the escape velocities of the planets are listed in Table 1.

Rotation Rates

As the planets move in their orbits around the Sun, they also rotate around their axes. The axis of a planet is the imaginary line that connects the planet's north pole to its south pole. The time it takes a planet to complete one rotation around its axis is called its rotation period. For planets with small inclinations (we shall get to this subject in the next section) the rotation period largely determines the length of a planetary day. Since it determines the length of time the Sun shines and the length of the night, the length of the planetary day is important in meteorology. In general, a point on a rotating planet will be sunlit half of each day. The length of a day on the Earth is about 24 hours. A planet with a 24-hour day will have, on the average, 12 hours of sunshine and 12 hours of night. The actual duration of sunshine will vary with latitude and season around this average value. This variation (which will be discussed later) is a result of the inclination of the planet.

The rotation periods for the planets are listed in Table 1. Until recently, the rotation period of Mercury was believed to be 88 days, which is exactly equal to the length of its year. This belief was based on telescopic observations of the rate of rotation of features on the surface of the planet and on theoretical computations. Very recently, however, radar observations of the planet's rotation rate have been made. They indicate, surprisingly, that Mercury's rotation period is not 88 days but about 59 days.

The startling result of the radar observations led scientists to go back to the previous telescopic observations and theoretical calculations. Because it is so close to the Sun, Mercury is a difficult object to observe telescopically. Features of the planet had been sketched by observers only a very few times. These sketches all looked alike, and scientists, therefore, had interpreted this sameness to mean that we were seeing the same side of Mercury all the time—just as we see the same side of the Moon all the time. They had concluded that the same side of Mercury always faced the Sun while the planet traveled its orbit, and that Mercury's rotation period was, therefore, equal to its orbital period of 88 days. But other interpretations of these few observational data are possible. For a simple example, suppose you were on another planet and were attempting to determine the rotation period of the Earth. You make three observations of the Earth at 24-hour intervals. Each time you see the same features on the Earth. You might conclude from your observations that the same side of the Earth always faces the Sun. On the other hand, you might interpret the observations as indicating rotation at one of several possible rates—a 24-hour period or a 12-hour period or an 8-hour period or a 6-hour period, for example. When scientists analyzed the few observational data on Mercury's rotation period, again they found, among other things, that a rotation period of 59 days agreed with the few visual sightings. Since a rotation period of 59 days also agrees with the radar observations, this new analysis puts the new value of Mercury's rotation period on firm ground. In addition, new theoretical work also supports a value of 59 days for Mercury's rotation period.

The rotation period of Venus is about 250 days. The length of its year is only 225 days. Thus, it takes Venus longer to complete one rotation around its axis than to make one complete trip around the Sun. Furthermore, the rotation is retrograde; that is, the sense of the rotation of Venus around its axis is opposite to the sense of its revolution around the Sun. Only one other planet, Uranus, is in retrograde motion.

If we could remove ourselves from the solar system to a position looking down on the planets' orbital plane, we would see all the planets, except Venus and Uranus, moving around the Sun in a counter-clockwise direction and rotating around their own axes in a counterclockwise direction. Venus and Uranus would rotate clockwise around their axes. This motion, combined with the long orbital period, causes the planet Venus to have only about two sunrises and two sunsets per year. Thus, the duration of daylight at any point on the surface of Venus is extremely long. The value given here for the rotation period of Venus is a recent finding, and if you do not completely understand it, you are in good company; astronomers also are trying to digest the implications.

The rotation periods of the other planets range from a rapid 9 hours 51 minutes for Jupiter to a leisurely 6 days for Pluto. Mars is almost the Earth's twin in this respect, having a rotation period of 24 hours 37 minutes.

The rotation of a planet affects its winds. To illustrate, imagine yourself at the center of a merry-go-round that is *not* moving. Suppose there is one toy horse on the merry-go-round, and that this horse is attached to the outer rim. Also suppose that a friend is standing on the ground near the outer rim of the merry-go-round, right behind the toy horse. You have a ball and want to show how good your aim is.

With the merry-go-round still stopped, you throw and, your eye being sharp, hit the horse. Your friend challenges you to repeat the hit when the merry-go-round is moving. At each revolution of the turning merry-go-round there is one instant when you, the horse, and your friend the observer are on the same straight line. You pick that instant to throw. The ball misses the horse but hits the observer. Why?

As the ball travels toward the horse, the horse is moving with the merry-go-round. The ball ends up to the right of the horse and in the hands of the observer, who, being on the ground, is not moving with the merry-go-round. With respect to the rotating merry-go-round the ball does not follow a straight line but describes a curve across the platform to the right of where you intended it to go. But with respect to the observer the ball follows a straight line from you to him. Thus, whether the ball curves to the right or follows a straight line depends upon the frame of reference. With respect to the observer's frame of reference the ball follows a straight line; with respect to the rotating frame of reference of the merry-go-round the ball is deflected to the right.*

Now, what can our merry-go-round experiment have to do with winds? A planet that did not rotate would be analogous to the stationary merry-go-round. Winds on a nonrotating planet are not de-

* This effect, of great importance in ballistics and oceanography as well as meteorology, is called the *Coriolis force* for its discoverer, the French mathematician and engineer Gaspard de Coriolis (1792–1843).

flected and travel in a straight line—both with respect to the planet and with respect to an absolute coordinate system fixed in space. But on a rotating planet winds are deflected from their initial directions with respect to the planet but not with respect to an absolute coordinate system fixed in space. With respect to space the deflection is fictitious. Since everyone on the planet is concerned with the direction of the wind with respect to the planet, this deflection is a very real one to them. Witness your own astonishment when the ball you threw in a straight line followed a curved course across the merry-go-round platform. This deflection is introduced by the planet's rotation. The strength of the deflection force depends upon the rate of rotation; the higher the rotation rate, the greater the deflection force.

Inclinations

The axis of a planet is generally *not* perpendicular to the plane of its orbit. The angle between the planet's axis and the perpendicular to the plane of its orbit is called its tilt or inclination. As a planet revolves around the Sun, its inclination remains the same in both amount and direction (Fig. 10). The inclination of the Earth's axis—23½ degrees—is quite commonly known. The inclinations of the other planets are listed in Table 1 and shown graphically in Fig. 9.

Since it determines seasonal variations in climate,

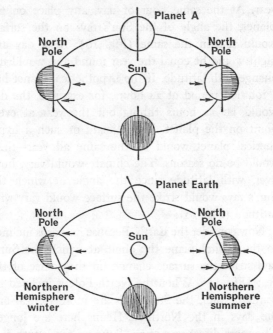

Fig. 10 *Planetary inclination and the seasons. On hypothetical planet A with no inclination the Sun's rays (arrows) strike any given region at the same angle all year round. Planet A has no seasons. On Earth, inclined at 23½°, the angle of the rays on a region changes through the year, producing the seasonal pattern of climate and growth.*

a planet's inclination is very important. To illustrate this effect, consider two planets—the first, a hypothetical planet with no inclination; and the second, the Earth. Since the hypothetical planet's axis is perpendicular to the plane of its orbit, the Sun's path in the sky would remain the same each day of the year. At the same hour of day, any place on the planet, the angle of the Sun's rays on the surface would remain the same (Fig. 10). Also, day and night would be equal the year round and would not change with latitude. If the hypothetical planet had a rotation period of 24 hours, for example, the day would be 12 hours throughout the year at every point on the planet. The climate of such a hypothetical planet would be the same all year—there would be no seasons. The climate would vary, however, with latitude since the angle at which the Sun's rays would strike the surface would vary with latitude (Fig. 10).

Now consider the Earth. Because its axis is inclined to the orbital plane the angle at which the Sun's rays strike the surface changes in the course of the year (Fig. 10). When the North Pole is inclined toward the Sun, the Sun's rays are more vertical and the days in the Northern Hemisphere are longer. The more direct rays of the Sun and the longer days cause warm weather. This is the summer season in the Northern Hemisphere. At the same time the Sun's rays are less vertical and the days are shorter in the Southern Hemisphere. This hemisphere is having its winter season. The changes in the angle of the Sun's rays and in the duration of daylight over the year are due to the Earth's inclination. Thus, it is the Earth's inclination that causes the seasons. Planets with inclinations larger than the Earth's should have greater seasonal variations; planets with smaller inclinations should have less pronounced seasonal variations.

From Table 1, it can be seen that Mars, Saturn, and Neptune all have inclinations between 20° and 30°. These planets should have seasonal variations comparable to the seasonal variations on Earth. This does not mean that the seasons will be similar; it means only that the *differences* between winter and summer will be comparable to that on Earth. Jupiter's inclination is only about 3°. Its axis is almost perpendicular to the plane of its orbit, and so its seasonal variations should be quite small. Uranus, on the other hand, has an inclination of 98°. Its axis is almost parallel to the plane of its orbit, and so its seasonal variations should be very large.

Albedos

The average temperature of a planet depends upon the amount of solar radiation it absorbs. At first thought, one might expect the amount of absorbed solar radiation to be equal to the amount striking the planet. This is not completely true, for some of the radiation is reflected back to space. Only the part not reflected back to space is absorbed. It is this fraction that heats up the planet. The ratio of the amount of reflected solar radiation to the amount of solar radiation striking the planet is called the albedo of the planet. Thus, the albedo of a planet influences its temperature.

The albedo of the Earth is about 0.35. This means that the Earth reflects about 35 per cent of the solar radiation striking it. The Earth's clouds do most of the reflecting, although the surface and atmospheric gases also contribute to the albedo. Clouds are very efficient reflectors of solar radiation, as anyone who has flown over them in an airplane can testify. Can you think of a surface condition that would have a very high albedo? If you thought of snow, you were right. The albedo of fresh snow may be as much as 81 per cent. If the Earth had a higher albedo than 35 per cent, its average temperature would be lower; if it had a lower albedo its average temperature would be higher. As we shall see later, there are other atmospheric properties—in particular, the so-called atmospheric greenhouse effect—that may influence a planet's temperature. For some planets, these atmospheric properties may increase the temperature above what one would expect from consideration of only the planet's albedo and distance from the Sun.

The albedos of all the planets are listed in Table 1. Venus has the highest, 0.73. This percentage is not surprising since the planet is completely covered with clouds. The planet with the lowest albedo is Mercury. It reflects only about 6 per cent of the solar radiation striking it. Since Mercury is so close to the Sun and since it reflects so little solar radiation, we can expect it to have a high temperature. In general, a low albedo indicates that a planet has few clouds and a small amount of atmosphere. The albedo of Mercury is about the same as the albedo of the Moon, which has essentially no atmosphere.

Chapter IV

THE ATMOSPHERE OF MARS

To those expecting to see networks of canals and multilane highways, interspersed with landing fields for flying saucers, the Mariner IV pictures must have been a disappointment. Scientists, on the other hand, found them little short of sensational. The prospect of what will be found when instruments, and eventually human observers, are landed on the surface of Mars, took on exciting new possibilities.

Appearance of Mars

Seen through a telescope, the Martian surface appears to be composed of three types of regions: (1) bright areas, reddish-orange in color, which occupy most of the surface and give Mars its nickname—the "red planet"; (2) dark areas, gray in color, which occur in patches; and (3) very white areas surrounding the poles (Plate III).

The dark areas and the white polar areas undergo seasonal changes. The relationship of these changes to weather conditions and the possibility of some form of life on Mars will be discussed later. The bright areas are believed to be similar to deserts on Earth. The dark areas were once thought to be oceans, but this speculation was dismissed when observations indicated that the dark areas do not reflect sunlight as water should. From time to time, clouds block the surface from view, but compared to the occurrence of the clouds in the Earth's atmosphere, such occasions are rare. Observations over many years are incorporated in the maps scientists have drawn of Mars (Plate IV).

The close-up pictures of Mars (Plate II) taken by Mariner IV indicate the presence of many moonlike craters, ranging in size from 3 to 75 miles, and possibly 200 miles, across. The photographs cover perhaps 1 per cent of the surface of Mars. From the number of craters identified, scientists estimate that the number of large craters on the planet may exceed 10,000. The rim of one gently sloping crater has been estimated to be 13,000 feet above the floor.

No Earthlike feature, no mountain chain, valley, ocean basin, or continental structure, has been detected in the pictures. The Martian craters presumably have been gouged out in the impacts of thousands of meteorites over the billions of years since the planet was formed. Why should Mars have so many craters on its surface compared to Earth? There are several reasons. As we shall see later, Mars has a much thinner atmosphere. More meteorites can penetrate to the Martian surface without burning up as most meteorites do in the Earth's atmosphere. Mars is also close to a region of the solar system—the asteroid belt—that is believed to be a source of meteorites. Being so close to a source, Mars probably comes into contact with meteorites more frequently than the Earth does. The absence of erosion and other destructive forces also would account for the existence of so many craters. On Earth such features as craters would not last long because of the action of weathering and natural Earth upheaval processes. Rain, wind, flowing rivers, mountain-building forces, and earthquakes quickly (on a geologic time scale, that is) wear down or crumble prominent ridges. On Mars, there are apparently no surface upheaval processes, and, as we shall see later, probably no rain or water on the surface. These are all good explanations of the presence of craters on Mars. Yet, no one predicted that Mars would look so much like the Moon from close up.* It took just the one set of close-up photographs to present the scientifically startling fact that Mars is covered with craters. This helps to prove the old saying, "One picture is worth a thousand words." (On the other hand, it has also been said, in connection with the possibility of life on Mars, "One word from Mars would be worth a thousand pictures.")

* A few scientists had hinted at this, however. Clyde W. Tombaugh said, in 1950, "The lack of water erosion on Mars would permit the surface to retain a visible record of the major events that happened during the planet's entire separate existence, similar to that on the Moon."

Atmospheric Composition

To determine the composition of the mixture of gases that Martian "air" is made of, astronomers have focused their spectrometers on radiation reflected from the planet. The spectrometer is a device to separate radiation into the spectrum of its component wavelengths. You have almost surely seen what a triangular glass prism does to sunlight. On passing through the prism the white sunlight separates into bands of color, from red through violet (Fig. 11),

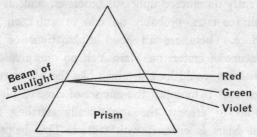

Fig. 11 *A glass prism separates a beam of sunlight into its component wavelengths or colors. The shorter the wavelength the greater the bending, which is called refraction. Astropyhsical observations are made on the same principle with more complicated instruments.*

one for each wavelength. The separation of the colors occurs because each wavelength undergoes a different amount of bending. The prism is a simple spectrometer.

You might think that a planet would reflect all colors of the solar radiation in equal amounts, but the fact is otherwise. At some wavelengths the amount reflected is less than at neighboring wavelengths. These reductions occur in absorption of the solar radiation on its double passage through the planet's atmosphere (Fig. 12). Different atmos-

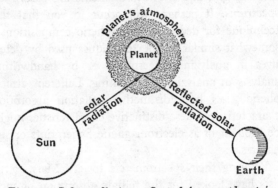

Fig. 12 *Solar radiation reflected from a planet is absorbed on its double pass through the planet's atmosphere. Earth-based measurements of the intensity of reflected solar radiation yield information on the gases in the planet's atmosphere. From such observations the composition of a planet's atmosphere can be estimated.*

pheric gases absorb at different wavelengths. By finding what wavelengths are missing—that is, the wavelengths at which absorption occurs—one can learn which gases are present in the planet's atmosphere. Furthermore, from a measurement of the amount of absorption at a particular wavelength, and a knowledge of the absorbing power of the gas (usually known from laboratory measurements), one can estimate the amount of this particular gas in the planetary atmosphere. This is a very powerful technique, for it enables us not only to identify the constituents of an atmosphere many millions of miles away, but also to estimate the amounts of various constituents. The general technique is called *spectroscopy*, and the measurements are *absorption spectrums*. It perhaps will occur to you that this technique for deducing atmospheric composition is somewhat similar to the techniques used by detectives in analyzing fingerprints or by handwriting analysts in analyzing handwriting. Different atmospheric gases have distinctive radiation absorption characteristics; these distinctive characteristics might be thought of as electromagnetic fingerprints or signatures.

Pointing their spectrometers toward Mars, scientists have looked for the telltale absorption of such possible atmospheric gases as oxygen; carbon dioxide; carbon monoxide; oxides of nitrogen; methane; ammonia; and water vapor. They have not been able to look for nitrogen, a major component of the Earth's atmosphere, because nitrogen absorbs only ultraviolet radiation, which is absorbed in the Earth's upper atmosphere and never reaches the spectrometer of the astronomers. From these searches we have been able to learn something about the composition of the Martian atmosphere.

Carbon dioxide is definitely one of the gases in the Martian atmosphere. The exact amount is still somewhat uncertain; recent measurements suggest that more than 50 per cent of the atmosphere is carbon dioxide.

Water vapor has been detected, but it is present only in very small amounts. Scientists denote the amount of moisture in an atmosphere by expressing it as the amount of liquid that would form if all the vapor above one unit of surface area were condensed. This amount of liquid water is called the *precipitable water* of the atmosphere. On Mars the precipitable water is only about 10^{-3} cm (less than $\frac{1}{1000}$ of an inch). On Earth the precipitable water is about 1000 times greater. The Martian atmosphere is very dry indeed. At least, we shall not have to take umbrellas with us when we visit the planet.

The search for other gases has produced negative results. If other gases are present at all, it is in extremely small amounts. Oxygen, which is so important to life on the Earth, is not part of the Martian atmosphere. Space crews landing on the planet will have to take along an oxygen supply.

So far, we have accounted for more than half of the atmosphere, which is in the form of carbon dioxide. What about the remainder? Nitrogen and argon are believed to be the other major constituents of the Martian atmosphere. Final determination of the atmospheric composition probably will have to await analysis with instruments transported into the atmosphere itself.

In summary, the Martian atmosphere seems to be composed mainly of carbon dioxide, with some nitrogen and argon. The Earth's atmosphere, in contrast, is composed mainly of nitrogen and oxygen.

A graphical comparison of the composition of both
atmospheres is shown in Fig. 13.

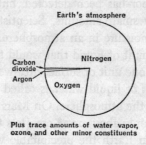

Fig. 13   *Pie graphs illustrating the composition of
the atmospheres of Earth and Mars. The atmosphere of Mars contains no oxygen.*

Temperatures

There are both observational and theoretical techniques for estimating a planet's temperature. Both
depend upon Planck's law,* which describes how

---

* Named for the great Max Planck (1858–1947), whose
work laid the foundation of quantum theory and opened
the door to much of modern physics.

the intensity of radiation from a radiating body at a particular temperature varies with wavelength. In other words, the law relates intensity of radiation, wavelength of radiation, and the temperature of the radiating body. Planck's law tells us that (1) the intensity of radiation at any wavelength increases with increasing temperature of the radiating body, and (2) the wavelength at which the maximum intensity occurs decreases with increasing temperature. Condition (1) states that a warm radiating body will emit more radiation than a cooler radiating body at all wavelengths. Condition (2) tells us at what wavelength the maximum intensity of radiation occurs; for a warm radiating body the maximum intensity occurs at a shorter wavelength than for a cool radiating body. Fig. 14 shows examples of intensity curves computed from Planck's law. One of these examples is a radiation intensity curve for the Sun, which is at a temperature of about 5500° C. (9932° F.); another is a curve for the Earth, which is at a temperature of about 15° C. (59° F.). The curve for the Sun is typical of stars, and the curve for the Earth is typical of planets. At all wavelengths solar radiation intensities are greater than planetary radiation intensities. Solar radiation peaks at a relatively short wavelength that is in the middle of the visible radiation range. The Earth's radiation peaks at a relatively long wavelength in the middle of the infrared range. Solar radiation is sometimes referred to as short-wave radiation, and the Earth's as long-wave radiation. In general, radiation from such high-temperature bodies as the Sun and stars is con-

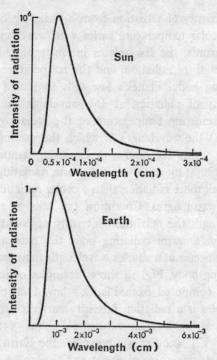

Fig. 14 *Radiation intensity curves computed from Planck's law. Note different intensity and wavelength scales. Solar radiation peaks at relatively short wavelength in middle of visible range; Earth's radiation peaks at relatively long wavelength in middle of infrared range. At wavelength of peak radiation, solar radiation intensity is 10^6 times larger than Earth's radiation intensity. Solar radiation intensities are greater than Earth's at all other wavelengths. (After D. Brunt,* Physical and Dynamical Meteorology, *Cambridge University Press.)*

centrated in the visible part of the electromagnetic spectrum, but there is also some radiation at shorter and longer wavelengths. Radiation from such relatively low-temperature bodies as the Earth and the other planets is concentrated in the infrared part of the spectrum. But if planetary radiation is largely infrared and infrared radiation is invisible, how can we see the planets? We see them because they reflect some of the Sun's visible radiation (sunlight) toward the Earth.

The temperature is a property of considerable importance in the study of planetary atmospheres. The observational technique of estimating a planet's temperature is to measure the intensity of radiation at a particular wavelength and with that value make a calculation from Planck's law. The computation must take into consideration, of course, the diminution of the planet's radiation in an amount proportional to the square of the distance from planet to Earth. There is also a theoretical technique based on the following line of reasoning.

We know that the Sun is the source of heat energy for all the planets. All the solar radiation that is not reflected back to space by a planet is available to heat the planet. Since the average planetary temperature remains constant from year to year, a planet must radiate to space, on the average, as much radiation as it receives from the Sun. The amount of solar radiation a planet receives from the Sun can be calculated easily. It depends upon the intensity (which is known) of radiation emitted by the Sun, upon the distance of the planet from the Sun, and the planet's albedo. From Planck's law one can compute the temperature at which the planet radiates as much energy to space as it receives from the Sun. This temperature is a theoretical estimate of the average temperature of the planet. In this manner, one can estimate the temperatures of all the planets.

Applied to Mars, this theoretical technique leads to a value of about −65° C. (−85° F.) for the average surface temperature. Measurements of the intensity of radiation emitted by the planet, at wavelengths that are not absorbed in either Mars' or the Earth's atmosphere, indicate, through Planck's law, that the actual average surface temperature is about −50° C. (−58° F.). Although still very cold, the observed temperature is higher than the theoretically estimated temperature. The cause of this disparity is the presence in the Martian atmosphere of a gas that absorbs some of the emitted infrared radiation and thus cuts down on the planet's loss of heat energy to space. The temperature rises to a level higher than it would reach if no absorbing gas were present. This effect occurs in all planetary atmospheres containing gases that absorb infrared radiation. It is called the *greenhouse effect* because it is similar to the influence of the glass walls and roof on the temperature within a greenhouse. The glass allows solar radiation to enter but inhibits infrared radiation from leaving the greenhouse. The gas in the Martian atmosphere that is responsible for the greenhouse effect is carbon dioxide. In the Earth's atmosphere water vapor, being a very powerful absorber of infrared radiation, is the most important

contributor to the greenhouse effect. If there were
no greenhouse effect in the Earth's atmosphere, the
average surface temperature would be a chilly $-20°$
C. ($4°$ F.) rather than the comfortable $15°$ C. ($59°$
F.) we now enjoy. It is to be noted that the greenhouse effect on Mars is much smaller than on Earth.

We all know that on Earth the temperature is
higher during the day, when the Sun is shining,
than it is at night, when the Sun has set. The difference between the maximum daytime temperature
and the minimum night temperature is called the
daily range of temperature. On the Earth a typical
value of the daily range for a sunny day is about $20°$
C. ($36°$ F.), although in desert regions the daily
range may be as high as about $50°$ C. ($90°$ F.). The
observations of Mars indicate that, in the equatorial
regions, the daily range of temperature may be as
great as $100°$ C. ($180°$ F.), or over twice the highest
daily range on the Earth. This temperature range
during a single day on Mars is greater than the temperature difference between the Earth's Arctic regions and its equatorial zone. One cause of the
larger variation on Mars is to be found in the small
amount of absorbing gases in the atmosphere. Without such absorbing gases, the infrared radiation
emitted by the surface escapes to space, and the surface cools quite rapidly during the night.

Just as on the Earth, the average yearly temperature on Mars is highest at the equator and decreases
toward the poles. A comparison of the latitudinal
variation of temperature for Mars and Earth during
the equinoctial seasons—that is, when it is autumn

in one hemisphere and spring in the other—is shown in Fig. 15. Also shown in these diagrams are the average maximum and minimum daily temperatures to be expected on Mars during these seasons. It is quite clear from these curves that although Mars is in general much colder than the Earth, the temperature during the day at the Martian equator may rise

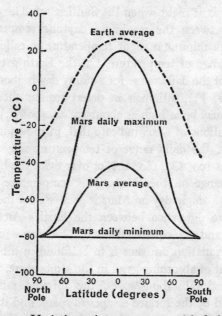

Fig. 15 Variation of temperature with latitude during the equinoctial seasons for Mars and Earth. Although Mars is generally colder than Earth, its equatorial regions may heat up to Earth-like temperatures during the daytime. (Mars temperatures after W. W. Kellogg. Courtesy of International Science and Technology.)

to a balmy 20° C. (68° F.), which, of course, is not by any stretch of the imagination an unearthly temperature. The latitudinal temperature variations at the solstices—that is, when one hemisphere is having winter while the other hemisphere has summer—are shown in Fig. 16. During winter the temperature is

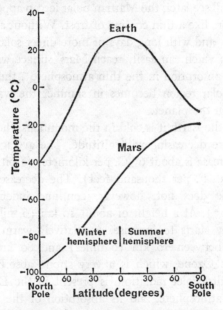

Fig. 16 *Variation of average temperature with latitude during Northern Hemisphere winter for Mars and Earth. On Mars, the hottest temperature in the summer hemisphere is at the pole, while on Earth the hottest temperature in the summer hemisphere is near the equator. (Mars temperatures after Y. Mintz. Courtesy of National Academy of Sciences.)*

highest at the Martian equator, just as on the Earth. During the summer, however, the average temperature on Mars is highest at the poles, rather than near the equator as on the Earth. The probable explanation of this difference is the lack of huge polar ice masses on Mars; the icecaps in our polar regions tend to keep polar areas cool even in summer. As we shall see later, the Martian polar icecap appears to be more like a thin coating of frost. Without a thick icecap, and with long days of more direct solar radiation (which can easily reach Mars' surface without much absorption in the thin atmosphere), the Martian polar region becomes in summer the warmest spot on the planet.

On the Earth it is cold in the mountains, the temperature decreasing with altitude. The average rate of decrease is about 6° C. per kilometer (a bit more than 3° F. per thousand feet). The decrease with altitude does not, however, continue indefinitely (Fig. 17). At a height of about 10 km (6 miles) it actually starts to increase. A relatively warm layer exists between 10 km (6 miles) and 80 km (50 miles). Ozone, which is a very strong absorber of solar ultraviolet radiation, is present in the Earth's upper atmosphere, and its absorption of the radiation heats the air at high levels. Since the Martian atmosphere has no ozone, we would not expect to find a comparable warm layer on Mars. Although scientists have not been able to measure the vertical variation of temperature in the Martian atmosphere, they have made estimates (Fig. 17). The conclusion is that no warm layer exists in the Martian upper at-

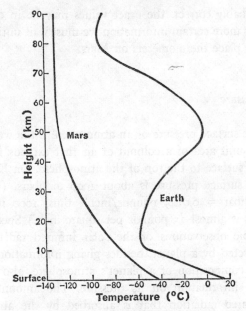

Fig. 17 *Variation of temperature with height in the atmospheres of Mars and Earth. In the Earth's upper atmosphere the presence of ozone, which is a very strong absorber of solar ultraviolet radiation, causes relatively high temperatures between 10 km and 80 km.*

mosphere. The temperature just keeps on decreasing with height. However, the rate of decrease is less at the higher altitudes.

Bear in mind that the Martian temperatures discussed in this section are based not on direct measurements, but either on deductions from the planet's radiation or on theoretical estimates. Although the main features of the temperature variation are probably correct, the exact values may be in error. For more certain information we must wait until we can place thermometers on Mars.

Pressure

The surface pressure of an atmosphere is the weight per unit area of a column of air that extends from the surface to the top of the atmosphere. On Earth the surface pressure is about 1000 millibars. (One millibar = 0.0145 pounds/inch^2; thus, 1000 millibars is almost 15 pounds per square inch.) Spectroscopic observations of the solar infrared radiation reflected by a planet, besides giving information on the composition of a planet's atmosphere, also can give information on its pressure. The amount of infrared radiation that is absorbed by the atmosphere depends upon its pressure—the higher the pressure, the greater the amount of absorption—and therefore determination of absorption gives a measure of pressure.

For a long time, the surface pressure on Mars was believed to be about 85 millibars. Recent spectroscopic observations suggest, however, that the surface pressure is lower—about 10 millibars. The most recent estimate of the surface pressure on Mars was derived from an ingenious experiment on the Mariner IV fly-by. By analyzing the radio signals received on Earth from Mariner just before the spacecraft disappeared behind Mars, scientists were able to determine the amount of bending of the radio rays

passing through the Martian atmosphere. Since the
degree of bending of the radio waves depends on the
amount of atmosphere, it is possible from such an
experiment to deduce the surface pressure. The
Mariner IV measurements are in good agreement
with the low values obtained from the recent spectroscopic observations. Thus, the indications are
that Mars has very little atmosphere, only about 1
per cent of the Earth's atmosphere. In the planet's
low escape velocity we undoubtedly can find the
cause of the sparseness of atmosphere. Since it was
first formed, much of Mars' original atmosphere
probably has escaped to outer space.

The higher in the atmosphere you are, the lower
is the atmospheric pressure. The explanation is simple—there is a smaller amount of atmosphere above
you. For example, if you climbed to the top of Mt.
Everest, you would find that the atmospheric pressure is only about one-fourth what it is at sea level.
To reach a level in the Earth's atmosphere at which
the atmospheric pressure is as low as on the surface
of Mars, you would have to climb about 30 km (18
miles)—about three times the height of Mt. Everest. Only our highest-flying planes attain this altitude.

The rate at which the atmospheric pressure decreases with height depends upon a number of factors. One factor is the force of gravity: the greater
the force of gravity, the more rapid the decrease of
pressure with height. This condition seems quite
natural. A planet with a strong force of gravity will
pull its atmosphere toward the surface. Now, since

the gravitational force is less on Mars than on Earth, one would expect atmospheric pressure to decrease less rapidly with height on Mars than on Earth. But there are other factors that come into play, among them the mean molecular weight of the atmosphere. Atmospheres composed of heavy gases will be drawn toward the surface. Another factor that influences the rate of pressure decrease is the atmospheric temperature. We know that hot air tends to expand and cold air to contract. This effect leads to a slower decrease of pressure with height in a hot air mass. Carbon dioxide, the major constituent of the Martian atmosphere, has a greater molecular weight than nitrogen, the major constituent of the Earth's atmosphere, and Martian atmospheric temperatures are

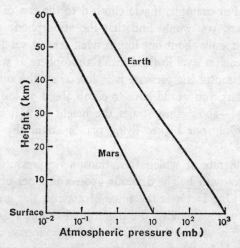

Fig. 18 Variation of atmospheric pressure with height in the atmospheres of Mars and Earth.

lower than Earth's atmospheric temperatures. Thus, these two factors would suggest that the atmospheric pressure decreases more rapidly with height on Mars than on the Earth. But when one takes into consideration all three factors—gravity, molecular weight, and temperature—one can show that pressure decreases with height on Mars at about the same rate as on Earth. The effect of gravity just about balances the effects of molecular weight and temperature. The variation of atmospheric pressure with height for both Mars and Earth is shown in Fig. 18. Martian atmospheric pressures are about $\frac{1}{100}$ of Earth's atmospheric pressures at all heights.

Winds

The basic cause of winds, which are nothing more than movements of the atmosphere, is a difference in atmospheric pressure between two points. Air tends to move from regions of high pressure to regions of low pressure. Everyday experience shows this. For example, when you release the valve of an automobile or bicycle tire, or when you let go the neck of a filled balloon, air is set in motion. The air rushes from a region of high pressure (within the tire or balloon) to a region of low pressure (the atmosphere outside the tire or balloon). Now, what causes pressure differences in a planet's atmosphere?

Consider a rotating planet. It is heated more strongly in its equatorial region than in its polar regions. The atmosphere heating up at the equator expands. At altitude the expanding air increases pressure and creates a pressure difference between the equator and the poles, the higher pressure being above the equator. The upper air, following the gradient from a region of higher pressure to a region of lower pressure, starts to flow toward the poles, where it sinks. The weight of this added air causes the *surface* pressure at the poles to be greater than the *surface* pressure at the equator. Thus, while upper air flows from equator to poles, the air near the surface moves from poles to equator. The resulting winds are shown in Fig. 19. You can see how the air

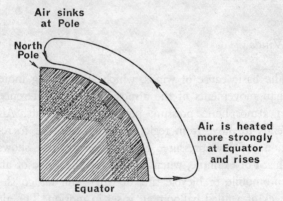

Fig. 19 Greater solar radiation at equatorial regions heats air more strongly than at poles. Heated air expands and rises, under pressure differences moves to poles at upper levels, toward equator at lower levels.

rises at the equator, moves toward the pole at high altitudes, sinks at the pole, and returns to the equator near the surface.

Plate I Mariner IV (NASA photo)

Plate II   This Mariner IV photograph of Mars covers an
area of about 170 miles in the east-west direction and about
150 miles in the north-south direction in the Atlantic
region, 31° south Martian latitude 163° west longitude.
North is at the top. (NASA photo)

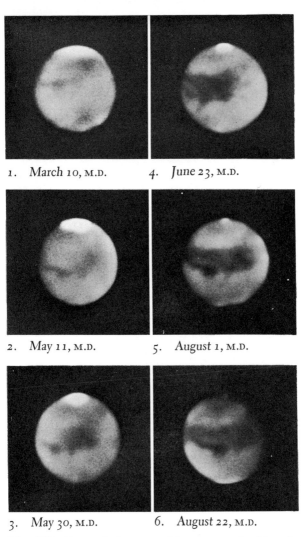

1. March 10, M.D. 4. June 23, M.D.

2. May 11, M.D. 5. August 1, M.D.

3. May 30, M.D. 6. August 22, M.D.

Plate III Seasonal changes on Mars are seen in this series of telescopic photographs. South pole is at top. Martian dates are indicated by letters M.D., with June 22, M.D. the beginning of summer in southern hemisphere. Dark areas become darker with melting of south polar ice cap. (Lowell Observatory photos)

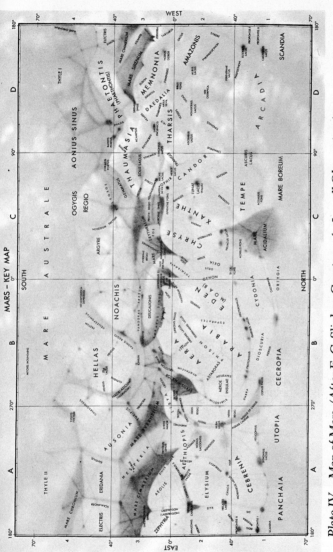

Plate IV   Map of Mars. (After E. C. Slipher. Courtesy of Lowell Observatory)

Plate V Venus at five different phases. *(Lowell Observatory photographs)*

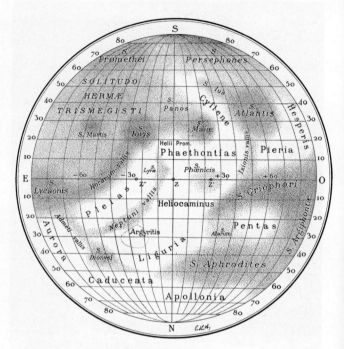

Plate VI   Map of Mercury (After E. M. Antoniadi.
Courtesy of Gauthier-Villars)

Plate VII Jupiter, showing its bands and Great Red Spot.
(Mount Wilson and Palomar Observatories photograph)

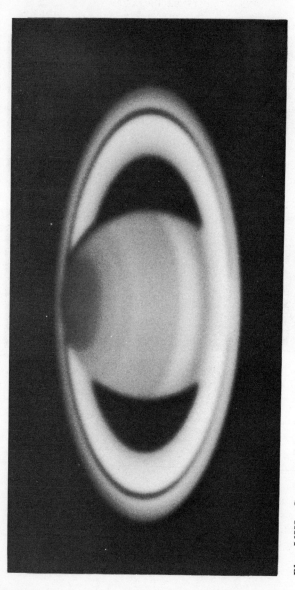

Plate VIII   Saturn and its rings. (Mount Wilson and Palomar Observatories photograph)

All this would happen if the planet were not rotating. But what is the effect of the planet's rotation? The Coriolis effect (Chapter III) does not allow the simple circulation described to persist by itself. The circulation that finally results represents a balance between the effect of the pressure differences (pressure gradient force) and the effect of the planet's rotation (Coriolis force). It is characterized by air spiraling poleward at upper levels in the atmosphere, and equatorward at low levels. This type of wind system (Fig. 20) is called a symmetrical cir-

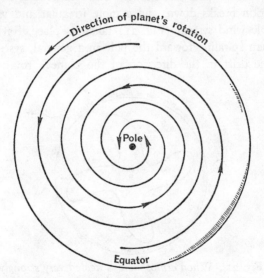

Fig. 20 *In symmetrical circulation pattern air spirals poleward at upper levels of the atmosphere, as shown here. At lower levels air would spiral toward the equator and airflow arrows would be reversed. (After Y. Mintz. Courtesy of National Academy of Sciences.)*

culation. It is a very simple, regular wind system. The net result of these winds is a transfer of heat from the hot equatorial regions to the cold polar regions. Without such a transfer of heat the equatorial regions would become unbearably hot while the polar regions were becoming unbearably cold.

The winds in the Earth's atmosphere are not so simple as those illustrated in Fig. 20. Theoretical studies show that if an atmosphere is heated very strongly at the equator compared to the poles, the symmetrical circulation cannot transfer heat from equator to pole fast enough. The symmetrical circulation breaks down, and a more irregular and variable wind system (Fig. 21) takes its place. Rather than spiraling toward the pole in a general, systematic drift in the direction of the planet's rotation,

Fig. 21 *When atmosphere is heated very strongly at the equator compared to the poles, a wave-type circulation pattern, similar to that shown above, develops. Such a wind pattern occurs in the Earth's atmosphere. (After Y. Mintz. Courtesy of National Academy of Sciences.)*

as in the symmetrical circulation, the air at upper atmospheric levels undergoes large north and south excursions as it drifts around the planet in the direction of the planet's rotation. This system, consisting largely of irregular wavelike patterns, is called a wave-type circulation. At one time the pattern of the motion may look like that sketched in Fig. 21. At some other time, this wavelike pattern will still be seen, but the number of "waves," the position of the "waves," and the shape of the "waves" may be different. It is this type that prevails in the Earth's atmosphere. The high and low pressure areas (storms) on a surface weather map are associated with these upper-level waves. These wave-type wind systems are very efficient in transporting heat from the equator toward the poles.

With this background on the different possible wind patterns, we are in a position to predict what system is likely to occur on Mars. Since Mars is a rotating planet, we would expect either a symmetrical circulation or a wave-type circulation. If the Martian atmosphere is heated very strongly at the equator compared to the poles, we would expect a wave-type circulation. If the rate of heating is only slightly higher at the equator, we would expect a symmetrical circulation. One recent study indicates that in the mean for the year the rate of heating is only slightly higher at the Martian equator, and hence a symmetrical circulation is likely to occur. But this study also suggests that during the Martian winter the symmetrical circulation breaks down and gives way to a wave-type circulation. Thus, this theoretical

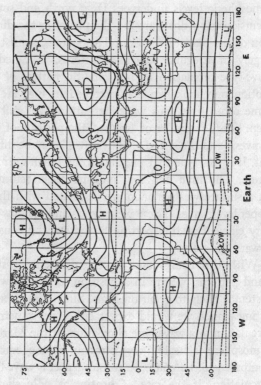

Fig. 22, a and b. Weather maps for Earth and Mars. Maps indicate surface-pressure pattern, with high-pressure areas indicated by letter H and low-pressure areas by letter L. Solid lines are isobars, or lines of constant pressure. Winds blow roughly parallel to the isobars, with low pressure to the left in Northern Hemisphere, to right in Southern Hemi-

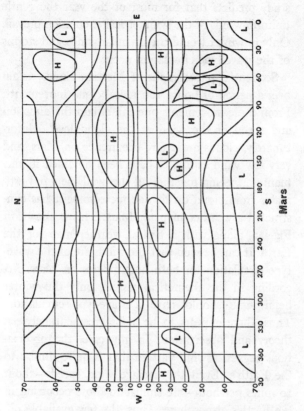

sphere. (Map for Earth is based on average sea level pressure distribution in January from Climatology, by B. Haurwitz and J. Austin, Copyright 1944, McGraw-Hill, Inc. Used by permission of McGraw-Hill Book Company. Map for Mars after S. Hess. Courtesy of American Meteorological Society.)

study predicts that for most of the year the gentle uniform winds of the symmetrical circulation prevail. Only in winter would the irregular winds and storms of the wave-type circulation occur.

Sequential photographs of Martian clouds, taken over a period of hours, can reveal cloud movements. From these movements one can obtain the direction and speed of the wind at the cloud level. Unfortunately, clouds are a rare occurrence on Mars, and very few wind estimates have been obtained in this manner. Piecing together all the available wind estimates from cloud drifts, one meteorologist has constructed a weather map for Mars. This is shown in Fig. 22, along with a typical weather map for the Earth. It can be seen that the winds are of the wave-type circulation for both hemispheres on Mars. According to the theoretical results, only the winter hemisphere should have a wave-type circulation. Thus, there appears to be a disagreement between theory and observation. In any case, the observations suggest a wind pattern that is quite similar to the Earth's. Even the average wind speeds—about 20 miles per hour—are similar to those occurring in the Earth's atmosphere. Thus, the few available observations suggest that Martian winds are not very different from winds on our home planet. An observer on Mars, however, would notice a difference. Because the pressure is less, the Martian atmosphere is lighter and the force of the wind would be less than on Earth. An observer could "feel" the difference between a Martian wind and an Earthly wind.

Clouds, Dust, and Storms

Clouds in the Earth's atmosphere are composed of either water droplets or ice crystals and occur frequently. On the average, clouds cover about 50 per cent of the Earth's sky. On Mars clouds occur infrequently, probably covering less than 10 per cent of the sky, on the average. The scarcity of clouds agrees well with the observations that only small quantities of water vapor exist in the atmosphere. The clouds that do occur on Mars are of three main types, white, blue, and yellow. Though rare, they at least appear to be more colorful than ours.

Of the three types, the white clouds occur most frequently. These brilliant clouds have been observed in equatorial, temperate, and polar latitudes. Over the poles they sometimes last several months; in temperate latitudes they may last for days or weeks. They are observed frequently at sunrise or sunset as thin, white mists. When the Sun is up, these thin mists quickly disappear. This behavior suggests that the thin white mists are nighttime events similar to the fogs that form on the Earth on cold, clear nights. Some white clouds seem to occur repeatedly over the same area. This repetition suggests that they may be due to upward air motions over mountains and hills, which would lead to condensation of any water vapor present in the atmosphere. Observations of the sunlight scattered by the white clouds suggests that they are composed of ice crystals, just like the cirrus clouds in the Earth's atmosphere.

Blue clouds occur at the winter pole, in the equatorial zone, and in favored locations. Frequently, they occur together with white clouds. There are indications that the blue clouds occur at higher altitudes than the white clouds. One scientist has estimated their heights at between 15 km (9 miles) and 25 km (15 miles) above the surface. Although no one is certain about it, the blue clouds are believed to be made of ice crystals.

Most spectacular of all the Martian clouds are the yellow clouds. Although appearing very infrequently, they sometimes grow to such size that they cover most of the planet from view. Occurring most often below a height of 8 km (5 miles), they have the same color as the reddish-orange deserts of Mars and may be composed of dust originating in those areas. The pattern of sunlight scattered by these yellow clouds is similar to the pattern of light scattered by tobacco smoke. If they are indeed dust clouds composed of particles from Martian desert regions, then we should be prepared to encounter an occasional dust storm or two on our eventual exploration of the planet.

The Blue Haze

Pictures taken of Mars in the blue region of the electromagnetic spectrum—that is, using a lens transmitting light with a wavelength less than 4.5×10^{-5}

cm—show no surface detail. There must be something in the Martian atmosphere that absorbs the blue part of solar radiation. The name "blue haze" has been given to this veiling of the surface. Occasionally, the Martian atmosphere clears up, and one can see the surface at these blue wavelengths. Oddly enough, the clearings seem to occur most often during that part of its orbit when Mars, Earth, and Sun lie in a straight line with the Earth in the middle. Suggestions for the composition of the blue haze have included carbon particles, fluorescing particles in the high atmosphere, meteoritic dust, and tiny ice crystals. But at the present time no one knows really what causes the blue haze, nor why it clears when it does.

Polar Caps, Waves of Darkening, and Canals

The most conspicuous features of the Martian surface are the brilliant, white polar caps. These caps undergo a very regular seasonal cycle. In the summer each cap covers only a tiny area at its pole. As autumn arrives, and along with it colder temperatures, the polar cap starts growing. The spreading continues until the end of winter when the cap may extend almost halfway to the equator. With the coming of spring and warmer weather the cap recedes. By summer it has all but disappeared. The cycle starts again as autumn arrives.

You will recognize in this regular behavior of the Martian polar regions a certain resemblance to our own Arctic region. In winter the Arctic is largely snow-covered. In spring and summer much of the snow melts, and the area covered by snow decreases. But there are important differences between the seasonal cycles on Mars and on Earth. On Earth the polar ice and snow even in summer cover a very large area, but on Mars the polar cap almost completely disappears in summer. Also, the extent of the Martian polar cap, at the height of its development, covers more of the planet than does the Earth's polar cap. Nevertheless, the similarity is so striking that the idea of ice- or snowcaps occurred to very early observers of Mars. But how to account for the almost complete disappearance in summer of an ice sheet that in winter may cover as much as half the hemisphere? It was suggested that the Martian ice sheet was only a few centimeters thick and that the increase in temperature between winter and summer would be sufficient to melt the entire cap. Recent observations have supported these suggestions.

Analysis of the fraction of the solar radiation reflected from the Martian polar caps indicates that the caps absorb radiation at the wavelengths characteristic of absorption by ice anywhere. Other analyses have shown that the solar radiation is reflected in a manner similar to the way ice reflects solar radiation. Although these observations are not positive proof, they certainly make a strong case for a polar cap consisting of ice. The discovery of a small amount of water vapor in the Martian atmosphere is also in agreement with a very thin polar cap composed of ice.

Of the three forms of water—water vapor, liquid

water, and ice—we have thus far suggested that two, water vapor in the atmosphere and ice in the polar caps, are present on Mars. What about liquid water? We have been skeptical of the existence of oceans on Mars. But how about small bodies of water, such as lakes or rivers? The laws of physics tell us that with the very small amounts of water vapor present above the Martian surface, liquid water cannot exist on the planet. For such small amounts any water substance must be either in the form of vapor or in the form of ice. When the icecap "melts" it changes directly to vapor without going through the liquid form. Thus, romantic hopes of picturesque lakes on Mars are not likely to be realized, and if we take along bathing suits on our trips to the planet, we shall have to be content with sunbathing.

There is a puzzle concerning the Martian polar caps and the water vapor in the Martian atmosphere. As we have seen, the total amount of water vapor in the atmosphere (the precipitable water) is about 10^{-3} cm. If all this vapor condensed into ice covering the entire planet, the ice would be only 10^{-3} cm thick. On the other hand, the polar icecap is estimated to be a few centimeters thick. With such a dry atmosphere how is it possible to form a polar cap even this thick? It has been suggested that at any one time most of the water substance on Mars is locked up in the polar caps—either in the northern hemisphere cap or in the southern hemisphere cap. According to this hypothesis, as one polar cap starts to melt, the water vapor released into the atmosphere is transported by atmospheric winds to the opposite pole, where it condenses again. Thus, there is a cyclic shuttling of water vapor from one pole to the other. As one icecap melts, the cap at the opposite pole is forming. Under such conditions polar icecaps could form despite the low atmospheric water vapor content. Whether this shuttle hypothesis is indeed the solution to the puzzle remains to be seen.

While the polar cap is melting during the spring, other regular changes occur on the planet. The dark areas near the cap become darker, changing color from gray to brown. As the melting continues, the darkening spreads toward the equator. By summer this "wave of darkening," as it is called, has affected all the regular dark areas in the summer hemisphere and reached the equator. In describing this seasonal change in color, an English astronomer, Patrick Moore, said, in 1958, that the dark areas behave as if they have been "roused from their deep winter sleep." And, indeed, many scientists believe that the wave of darkening is due to the growth of some form of primitive vegetation in the Martian dark areas. They suggest that as the icecap melts, water vapor is released into the dry atmosphere. The water vapor then moves toward the equator. With moisture available, and with the rising temperatures of spring and summer, the Martian vegetation begins to grow. Such a growing season would be quite similar to the vegetative growth cycle on Earth.

Measurements of the sunlight reflected from the dark areas indicate significant differences in the reflected light before and after the wave of darkening occurs. No such change occurs in the Martian bright areas. Some scientists do not agree with this theory of growing vegetation. They suggest that the wave of darkening may come from absorption, by surface salts, of water vapor released from the polar caps, or possibly from absorption of solar ultraviolet radiation, by surface minerals, as the Sun returns in the spring to the polar areas. But if the dark areas are not living matter, would not dust from atmospheric storms cover them? They no longer would be dark areas but would resemble the bright desert areas. The plain fact that the dark areas do remain from year to year and do not become covered with dust suggests that some form of vegetative life is able to grow through any layer of dust. The most recent evidence for vegetative life in the dark areas came from an analysis of the infrared radiation reflected by these areas. The dark areas, according to this study, absorb infrared radiation at precisely the same wavelengths as does certain organic matter. (Organic matter is material that is presently alive or was once alive. Coal is an example of organic matter that was once living vegetation.) This last piece of evidence, combined with the other evidence, convinced many scientists that vegetative life exists in the dark areas on Mars. Unfortunately, careful reanalysis of these observations revealed that a certain form of water vapor in the Earth's atmosphere could cause the observed absorption spectrum. But this explanation has certain difficulties. It does not explain why the absorption should be noted during observations of the Martian dark areas and not during observations of the bright desert areas. It also does not explain why the absorption was not noted during similar observations of the Sun. Thus, the real explanation of the observed absorption spectrum remains beyond our grasp.

Although the chances appear to be good that there is at least some form of vegetative life on Mars, this modest prediction is a far cry from the belief of several scientists around the turn of the century that not only was life present, but that it was present in the form of intelligent Martians. This belief was based upon occasional observations, during exceptionally good viewing conditions, of a regular pattern of lines on Mars. These lines were called canals. Several scientists believed that these canals were actually part of a huge irrigation system to drain water from the melting polar caps and make it available for farming on this very dry planet. One observer went as far as to work out the form and power of the pumping stations that would be required for this huge irrigation system. However, most observers today believe that the Martian lines or canals do not exist at all. Mariner IV passed by a region of "canals," but the pictures showed nothing remotely resembling canals. The observed lines may be no more than a series of separate dots and patches that the eye sees as a line. Even if there are such lines on the Martian surface, no one seriously believes them to be the work of a Martian civilization. With no water, no oxygen, and frigid temperatures, the planet seems too inhospitable for a Martian civilization to have developed. If there is life, it is most probably in the form of Martian vegetables.

Summary

When our space explorers land on Mars, they will have to contend with an atmosphere that has very little water vapor, large quantities of carbon dioxide, and, probably, nitrogen, but no oxygen. The atmospheric pressure will be as low as that prevailing in our own atmosphere at a height of 18 miles. In general, it will be extremely cold, with an average temperature of about −50° F. This picture is not too discouraging, but how will they adjust to a diurnal temperature difference of 180° F.? They can expect winds, but we do not know whether they will be as variable as those occurring on Earth. They should have fine weather for sightseeing; clouds will occur rarely. They will not have to worry about rain- or snowstorms, but should be prepared to face occasional severe dust storms. The surface will be completely dry, unless the landing is made on the polar icecap. Even here we can expect at most only a few inches of ice. The only life we can reasonably expect is a low form of vegetation. On the whole, it must be said that the planet does not appear to be too inviting. But, then again, neither is the top of Mt. Everest, which has been the goal of a number of human expeditions. And, in the case of Mars, there is still the possibility of encountering surprises more exotic than Abominable Snowmen.

Chapter V

THE ATMOSPHERE
OF VENUS

The planet Venus has been called the Earth's twin or sister planet. They are of about the same size and have almost the same mass. Apart from the Moon, Venus is our closest neighbor in space. You might think that because Venus is so close to the Earth, we should know a great deal more about it than about the other planets. Unfortunately, this is not strictly true. An extensive and permanent cloud cover has hidden many of Venus' secrets from man's view. It is only in recent years that measurements in the infrared and radio wavelength regions of the electromagnetic spectrum have given us a peek behind the veil.

Appearance of Venus

Since Venus lies between the Earth and the Sun, it shows phases, similar to the phases of the Moon, as it revolves in its orbit. The situation is shown in Fig. 23. When Venus is closest to the Earth, it lies directly between the Sun and the Earth. In this po-

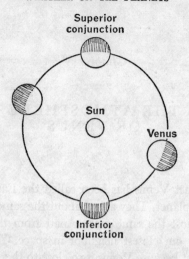

Fig. 23   The phases of Venus. At inferior conjunction, Venus cannot be seen from Earth.

sition, called inferior conjunction, Venus has its dark or night side toward us, and we cannot see it. When Venus is farthest from the Earth, the Sun lies directly between Venus and the Earth. In this position, called superior conjunction, Venus has the whole of its sunlit or daylight side toward us. From the Earth, we see Venus in different shapes at different times as the planet goes through its *phases*. The appearance and apparent size of the planet at various positions in its orbit are sketched in Fig. 24. Unfortunately, when Venus is closest to the Earth and has its largest apparent size, we cannot see it because the dark side is toward us. This situation is represented by the completely black circle in the illustration. As more and more of the planet becomes visible, the apparent size of the planet decreases. By the time Venus has reached superior conjunction and the entire planet is visible, the apparent size has decreased so much that Venus appears smaller than the distant planet Saturn.

Fig. 24 The apparent size of Venus at various phases.

Seen through the telescope, Venus is something of a disappointment. It appears as a very bright but almost completely featureless body (Plate V). With very careful observation, one occasionally can make out faint dark shadings. These shadings are not permanent but seem to form and disappear quite rapidly. When Venus is photographed in ultraviolet light, dark hazy patches show up. These patches change their form from day to day, suggesting that they represent features in the planet's atmosphere rather than permanent features on the planet's surface. In fact, the extreme brightness of the planet, the faint lemon-yellow color, the lack of permanent markings, and the variable markings in ultraviolet light, all suggest that when we observe Venus we are seeing not its surface but rather a permanent cloud cover in its atmosphere.

Atmospheric Composition

Spectroscopic measurements indicate that a small amount of the atmosphere consists of carbon dioxide. The actual estimates range between about 2 and 10 per cent. Until lately carbon dioxide had been the only gas definitely identified, but two recent spectroscopic searches for water vapor have been successful. Both searches were carried out from high-altitude balloons—one manned and one unmanned —in the Earth's atmosphere. Since the balloons were above most of the water vapor in the Earth's atmosphere, the spectroscopic observations were not contaminated by the variable water vapor amount in our own atmosphere. About 10^{-2} cm (.004 in.) of precipitable water was detected. Since this measurement is based upon solar radiation reflected by the Venus cloud top rather than the Venus surface, the deduced amount of water vapor refers only to the amount above the clouds. Its quantity is roughly comparable to the water vapor content of the upper part of the Earth's atmosphere. Undoubtedly, there is more water vapor in the atmosphere below the clouds, but, just as on Earth, water is a minor constituent, occupying no more than about $\frac{1}{100}$ of 1 per cent of the atmosphere of Venus.

Search for other gases, such as oxygen, has proved unsuccessful. Thus, as in the case of Mars, we can account for only a part of the entire atmosphere—the part composed of carbon dioxide. Again, as in the case of Mars, the remainder of the atmosphere is usually assumed to be composed of nitrogen. The composition of the Venusian atmosphere is diagramed in Fig. 25. Any traveler to Venus, like ex-

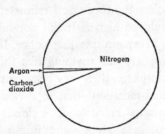

Plus trace amounts of water vapor and
possibly other minor constituents

Fig. 25   Pie graph illustrating estimated composition of the atmosphere of Venus.

plorers of Mars, will have to take along his own oxygen supply.

Temperature

A theoretical estimate of the surface temperature of Venus—based upon its distance from the Sun and its albedo of 0.73—yields a value of about –35° C.

(-31° F.). Since this estimate does not take into consideration the greenhouse effect of the planet's atmosphere, we would expect the actual surface temperature, as on Earth or Mars, to be somewhat higher than the theoretical estimate. What do the observations indicate?

As long ago as 1924, measurements were made of the infrared radiation emitted by the planet. They indicated a temperature of about -38° C. (-36° F.). These measurements have been repeated since that time with similar results. The observed temperature is slightly below the theoretical estimate, whereas it actually should be higher. It did not take long for astronomers to explain this discrepancy. If the clouds in the atmosphere are anything like the clouds in our own atmosphere, then they behave as black bodies for infrared radiation—that is, they absorb completely all infrared radiation. The clouds in the Venusian atmosphere absorb the infrared radiation emitted at the surface of the planet and reradiate it to space at the temperature of the cloud top. Thus, observations of the infrared radiation from Venus refer not to the surface of the planet but rather to the cloud tops, which have a lower temperature than the surface. The temperatures deduced from such observations are cloud temperatures, not surface temperatures. By this explanation the discrepancy between the theoretical estimate and the observed temperature is removed.

In the last ten years, astronomers have turned their radio telescopes toward Venus. These telescopes measure the radiation emitted by Venus in the microwave (radio) region of the electromagnetic spectrum. Microwave radiation has an interesting property: it can pass freely through clouds without being absorbed. Thus, observations of the microwave radiation from Venus should refer to the surface of the planet, and, by analysis of such observations, we should be able to deduce the actual surface temperature. The first of these observations were made by three American astronomers—C. H. Mayer, T. P. McCullough, and R. M. Sloanaker. The results were surprising. They indicated a surface temperature of over 300° C. (572° F.), well over the boiling point of water and uncomfortably close to the melting point of lead—327° C. (621° F.). These early results were confirmed by later observations. Scientists had expected a temperature higher than the theoretical estimate of –35° C., but not this much higher.

How does one explain such a high surface temperature? Three different hypotheses have been suggested.

The first suggests that the microwave radiation does not come from the surface of Venus at all. But if it doesn't come from the surface where does it come from? This hypothesis says that the microwave radiation originates in the very high atmosphere of Venus, in the ionosphere. The ionosphere of a planet is a layer in the planet's upper atmosphere that contains many electrically charged particles. According to this hypothesis, the ionosphere of Venus is at a very high temperature, greater than 300° C., and has an extremely large quantity of electrically charged particles. Under such conditions, the ionosphere is capable of emitting the large amount of microwave radiation that is observed from Earth. Thus, this hypothesis suggests that when we observe the microwave radiation from the planet, we are measuring the temperature of the planet's hot ionosphere rather than the temperature of the planet's surface. If this hypothesis is true, then the actual surface temperature is probably much less than a broiling 300° C.

A second hypothesis suggests that the observed high surface temperature is due to the very strong greenhouse effect of the planet's atmosphere. The large amount of carbon dioxide and the water vapor in the atmosphere would be barriers to the escape of most of the surface heat radiation to space. Furthermore, if the clouds of Venus are similar to Earthly clouds, they will readily transmit any unreflected solar radiation to the surface but will prevent the heat radiation emitted by the surface from escaping to space. And since the clouds on Venus apparently cover the entire sky, their contribution to the greenhouse effect should be substantial.

According to the third hypothesis, the atmosphere under the cloud layer may consist of swirls of dust kept in constant motion by winds above the clouds. Because of the huge quantities of dust, all solar radiation is absorbed in the atmosphere before reaching the surface. The wind-driven dust rubs against the planet's surface and by frictional heating raises the temperature of the surface. As in the greenhouse model, the heat radiation from the surface is prevented from escaping to space—not by carbon dioxide, water vapor, or clouds, but by the large quantities of dust, which efficiently absorb the surface radiation. If this hypothesis is correct, we would expect to find, on landing on Venus, no sunlight but plenty of dust, heat, and wind. This is not a very encouraging outlook at all.

Which of these three hypotheses, if any, is correct? At the present time we are still not certain, but we have been able to narrow down the choice. The Mariner II probe of 1962, forerunner of Mariner IV, passed within 22,000 miles of Venus and scanned both the dark and light sides. One experiment on the spacecraft was designed to determine whether the surface or the ionosphere was at the high temperature of over 300° C. The experiment was quite simple. While the spacecraft was passing Venus, the microwave radiometer on board first looked straight down toward the surface (Fig. 26) and then looked at an angle toward the edge of the planet and the atmosphere above it. In the first position it observed mainly radiation coming from the surface. In the second it observed mainly radiation from the atmosphere. A higher reading in the first position would indicate a hot surface; a higher reading in the second position would indicate a hot ionosphere. Mariner's radiometer took a higher reading in the first position, thus eliminating the hot ionosphere hypothesis. The measured surface temperature confirmed Earth-based observations. In fact, the Mariner observations suggest an even higher surface temperature of 427° C. (800° F.). But whether the high surface

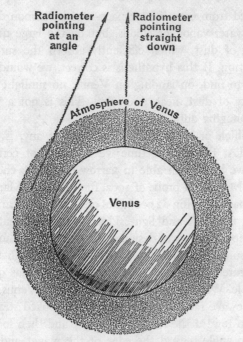

Fig. 26 As the Mariner II spacecraft flew by
Venus, the microwave radiometer was first pointed
straight down toward the surface, then at an angle,
to determine the source of the high-temperature
radiation from Venus.

temperature is due to a strong greenhouse effect or
a dust bowl—or possibly some other mechanism—
we still do not know.

Radio telescope observations also suggest that the
difference between the night and day temperature
on the surface of Venus may be as much as 300° C.
to 400° C. (540° F. to 720° F.). Thus, although the

average temperature of the planet is about 427° C. (800° F.), the hottest part of the sunlit side may have a temperature as high as 627° C. (1161° F.), while the coldest part of the dark side may have a temperature as low as 227° C. (441° F.). We must remember, however, that a night on Venus is quite long, over a hundred Earth days, since the planet rotates hardly at all; Venus takes roughly the same amount of time to complete one rotation around its axis as it takes to complete one revolution around the Sun. So if we are on the hottest place on the planet, the 300° C. to 400° C. change in temperature that we shall experience from day to night will occur over a relatively long time period. (For the sake of illustration, the temperatures listed are given to the nearest degree, but the uncertainties associated with these temperatures, as the discussion suggests, is in the neighborhood of 180° F.)

What keeps the temperature of the dark side so high—greater than at least 227° C. (441° F.)—through such a long night? Even with a strong greenhouse effect, the dark side should cool off considerably, one might think. The explanation here is the same as for our own Arctic areas, whose nights, exactly at the poles, last as long as six months. There is a constant transfer of heat by the winds from the sunlit side of Venus to the dark side just as there is a constant transfer of heat from the equatorial regions to the polar regions in our own atmosphere. This atmospheric process prevents the temperature on the dark side from decreasing further.

We should expect the temperature pattern on the

surface of Venus to be similar to that of a nonrotating planet. For such a planet the temperature would be highest directly below the Sun (the subsolar point) and would decrease in all directions from this point, as illustrated in Fig. 27. The lowest tempera-

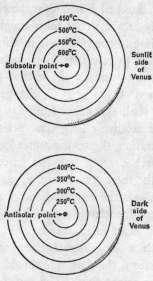

Fig. 27 Temperature patterns on Venus, both light and dark sides, according to current view.

ture would be at the antisolar point, which is on the dark side of the planet directly opposite the subsolar point. At the present time, techniques for obtaining such measurements with Earth-based radio telescopes are being developed, and our expected temperature distribution on the surface may soon be confirmed by observation.

The vertical variation of temperature in the atmosphere of Venus has recently been estimated (Fig.
28). This estimate is based largely upon the indi-

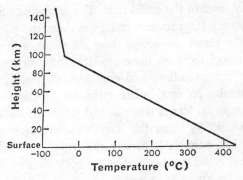

*Fig. 28   An estimate of the variation of tempera-
ture with height in the atmosphere of Venus.*

cations of surface and cloud temperatures obtained
from the microwave and infrared observations.
There is quite a bit of uncertainty here; no one really
knows the altitude of the cloud layer. The height of
the clouds is associated with the surface pressure,
about which we know very little. What little we do
know, we shall now discuss.

Pressure

You will recall (page 64) that absorption of infrared
radiation increases as the atmospheric pressure on
a planet increases. By analyzing the infrared reflection spectrum of a planetary atmosphere, scientists

can obtain estimates of atmospheric pressures. This
kind of observation has led to an estimate of 10,000
millibars for the surface pressure on Venus and between 90 millibars and 600 millibars for the pressure
at the level of the cloud tops. The estimated surface
pressure is large indeed, being ten times the pressure
on the Earth. However, there are many uncertainties associated with these available observations and
their interpretation, and the derived pressures are
uncertain. In fact, other estimates of the surface
pressures on Venus range as high as 50,000 millibars,
which is fifty times the Earth's surface pressure. If
this last estimate is correct the surface pressure on
Venus is the same as that at the bottom of a column
of water about 1600 feet high!

There is also a calculation involving surface and
cloud-top temperatures and other terms by which
one can obtain an estimate of the *minimum* possible
height of the clouds above the surface of Venus. According to this calculation, the clouds are at least
46.5 km (29 miles) high, and probably at greater
altitude. The average top of the clouds in our own
atmosphere is only 5 km (about 3 miles) high.

In the last chapter, we saw that the rate at which
atmospheric pressure decreases with altitude depends upon the force of gravity, the molecular
weight of the atmosphere, and the atmospheric
temperature. The force of gravity and the mean
molecular weight of the atmosphere are about the
same for Venus and Earth. Temperatures in the upper part of the atmosphere are also similar for both
Venus and Earth. Thus, in the upper part of the

Venusian atmosphere, the rate of pressure decrease should be the same as in the Earth's upper atmosphere. But in the lower part of the atmosphere of Venus, where the temperatures are so high, the atmospheric pressure will decrease less rapidly with height than it does in the Earth's atmosphere.

Winds

Since Venus rotates so slowly, we can consider it to be a nonrotating planet as far as its wind systems are concerned. As discussed in the section on temperatures, the hottest place on such a planet is the subsolar point and the coldest place the antisolar point. We have already described, in the chapter on Mars, the type of wind pattern that starts to form on a planet that is heated most strongly at its equator and least strongly at its pole (Fig. 19). Using the same reasoning as before, we would expect the air on Venus to rise over the subsolar point, move toward the antisolar point at high levels, sink near the antisolar point, and return to the subsolar point near the surface. Fig. 29 illustrates this expected atmospheric wind system. Now, since we can consider Venus to be a nonrotating planet, the pattern shown in Fig. 29 would not be deflected due to rotation of the planet, and should actually occur. The transport of heat that is necessary to keep the dark-side temperatures from dropping further during the long Venus night is accomplished in these atmospheric motions.

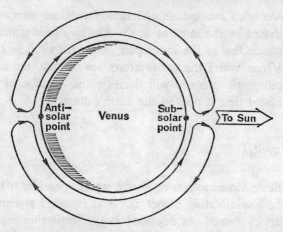

Fig. 29 Expected atmospheric circulation pattern on Venus.

The wind pattern described is based upon theoretical expectations. Unfortunately, it is extremely difficult to check our theoretical prediction with available observations. Since the cloud cover of Venus is a uniform layer, it is not possible, as it is in the case of Mars, to track individual cloud systems for the purpose of deducing winds. There are, however, some observational indications of wind patterns. A French astronomer, A. Dollfus, has reported seeing a radial cloud pattern centered on the subsolar point. If we assume that the winds are parallel to the radial cloud lines, the resulting wind pattern would be quite similar to the one predicted by theory. On the other hand, observations in ultraviolet light occasionally indicate straight cloud bands that are parallel to the equator on Venus. If

we again assume that the winds are parallel to the
observed cloud bands, the resulting wind pattern
would be more like the one prevailing in our own
atmosphere. Thus, the available observations are not
much help.

Clouds

On the Earth a prediction of the amount of cloudiness is one of the most difficult tasks a weather
forecaster has to perform. On Venus it would be
quite simple. The forecast would always be the same
—overcast skies. It is difficult to understand what
sort of atmosphere can maintain a permanent cloud
cover. In our own atmosphere most clouds are
formed as a result of the condensation of water vapor into droplets or ice crystals when air rises, expands, and cools off. If clouds in the atmosphere of
Venus form in a similar manner—that is, by condensation in rising air currents—the air would have
to rise all over the planet in order to maintain the
complete cover. But this situation could not exist,
for if air rises in one place it must come down in
another.

Clouds can form without the presence of rising
motions if the temperature is lowered sufficiently
—for example, by nighttime cooling—for condensation of water vapor to occur. Nighttime fogs and
stratus clouds on Earth form in this manner. Now,
it may be that in the atmosphere of Venus the temperatures are always low enough for water vapor, or

perhaps some other gas, to condense and form a permanent cloud cover. But this tidy explanation has a hole in it. Once such a cloud has formed, the cloud droplets or crystals will start to fall slowly. It may take a long time, but eventually all the cloud particles will either reach the ground or (more probably) evaporate in the warm air of the lower atmosphere. Further condensation and cloud formation may occur at the cloud level. But, again, the cloud particles eventually will fall out. Such a process of cloud formation can continue only as long as there is a sufficient amount of condensable gas at the cloud level. Eventually, this limit will be reached, and at that time there would be no further cloud formation in the atmosphere of Venus. A cloud formed in this manner could last indefinitely only if the supply of condensable gas were replenished from below. But, as in the case of clouds formed as a result of rising motions, this replenishment would require upward motion of the air all over the planet, an impossible condition to satisfy. So, the presence in the atmosphere of Venus of a permanent and complete cloud cover is extremely difficult to explain by a condensation process. The alternative explanation—that the cloud is formed of a noncondensable substance such as dust—also has difficulties. It is difficult to think of a continuous dust storm that could support a permanent dust cloud rising at least 40 km (25 miles) above the surface. The true explanation for the permanent shroud on Venus is still to be found.

Since the cloud layer is all we can see of Venus, it is ironic that we should not know what the clouds are made of. Analysis of the sunlight reflected to Earth from these clouds suggests that they probably are composed of ice crystals (Fig. 30). These observations are difficult to interpret, however, and the presence of dust clouds also has been offered as an explanation of the reflected radiation observed.

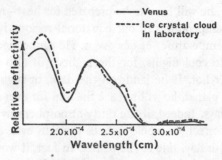

Fig. 30 *Radiation reflected from the clouds of Venus compared to radiation reflected from an ice crystal cloud in the laboratory. (After M. Bottema, W. Plummer, J. Strong, and R. Zander. Courtesy of University of Chicago Press.)*

There have been several other hypotheses for the make-up of the clouds: carbonate salts, smoglike mixtures, and chemical clouds consisting of carbon-oxygen mixtures. To confuse the matter still further, some recent observations raise the possibility that there might be a lower cloud layer underneath the cover we see with our telescopes. Hydrocarbons have been suggested as the major constituent of the lower layer. The ice hypothesis seems to be in favor at this writing.

Summary

The prospect of a trip to Venus is not very inviting. But if, in due course, some explorer with far better equipment than exists today should land on the planet, he will have to be prepared for heat—not the high temperatures of our equatorial regions but the high temperatures of our ovens. He cannot look forward to cool nights, for the nights will also be extremely hot. If he lands on the dark, or night, side of the planet, he will not see the Sun for over a hundred days. Indeed, if the dusty atmosphere hypothesis is correct, he would not see the Sun even on the sunlit, or day, side of the planet. In fact, it would be almost as dark as the night side. If the greenhouse hypothesis is correct, there is a chance that he would be able to see a dim outline of the Sun through the ever-present cloud layer. More likely, however, he would see only a dull, gray sky. A portable oxygen supply will be a necessity, for he could not exist very long without it in Venus' nitrogen-carbon dioxide atmosphere. To be on the safe side, he should wear a diving suit; the pressure may be as great as it is 1600 feet deep in our oceans. Is there a chance of his finding an ocean, or lake, or pond? Probably not. At such high temperatures, any liquid water that may have been present on the surface has probably boiled away. With our present estimates of the winds, we would expect him to encounter, near the surface, steady breezes blowing toward the subsolar point. Because of the higher atmospheric pressures, the force of the winds would be much greater than on Earth. If the dusty-atmosphere hypothesis is correct, the air will be filled with swirling dust.

All in all, Venus appears to be a very hostile world, indeed. But we shall never know for sure how hostile until we manage to penetrate the mysterious cloud cover that so far has hidden Venus' surface and lower atmosphere from man's view.

point. Therefore, if the high temperature observed is
the result of the winds, would be stabilize, rather than
on Earth. If this atmosphere indeed have oscillations, we
seen, the sun will be filled with existing distinct

Although Venus appears to be a very hostile world,
indeed, there is that there exist a now rough, less hostile
primitive means to penetrate the upper clouds and
explore the surface below. Below us, Venus' surface and
lower atmosphere on it is fully.

Chapter VI

THE ATMOSPHERES OF THE OTHER PLANETS

The factor of uncertainty increases when we turn our instruments from Mars and Venus toward the more distant planets of the solar system, but there are things we think we know about their atmospheres, and there are things we *know* we know. For an orderly approach, we shall begin with Mercury, which of all the planets lies closest to the Sun, and then move outward from Mars to Jupiter and, in turn, Saturn, Uranus, Neptune, and Pluto.

Mercury

Mercury is the fourth brightest planet, coming after Venus, Mars, and Jupiter, but it is not an easy one to observe. It is relatively small and far away. Because of its closeness to the Sun, Mercury too "goes down" when the Sun has disappeared over the horizon, and astronomical observations from the Earth must be made in daylight. The traditional picture of the astronomer's lonely vigil through the night does not apply in the case of Mercury. From what you have learned in our discussion of radiation, you will be quick to guess that daytime observation of the planet is extremely difficult. The solar radiation reflected from the planet toward us is in competition (from our point of view) with the far more intense direct radiation from the Sun itself.

Nevertheless, despite the difficulties, astronomers have drawn maps (Plate VI) of Mercury showing observed surface features consisting of light and dark areas. These maps probably refer to only one side of Mercury (Chapter III). It has been suggested that the surfaces of the Moon and Mercury may be alike, but we know very little about the planet's features.

There may be some question whether Mercury deserves to be discussed in this book at all, for the presence of an atmosphere on the planet is somewhat in doubt. Because of its low escape velocity, Mercury has lost most of any atmosphere it may have had in the past. If Mercury has an atmosphere, it can be only a thin one, composed of relatively heavy gases. The observational evidence does support the inference that Mercury has such a thin atmosphere. This evidence consists of: (1) occasional veiling of the surface, presumably caused by some sort of atmospheric clouds, and (2) reflected radiation from which has been deduced the existence of a surface pressure equal to about $\frac{3}{1000}$ of the Earth's surface pressure. Such a low pressure corresponds to the pressure in a laboratory vacuum; in the Earth's atmosphere one would have to ascend about 30 miles to find such a low pressure. Spectroscopic observations have suggested recently the presence of carbon dioxide in Mercury's neighborhood. The amount detected is sufficient to account for all the planet's thin atmosphere. In other words, the atmosphere of Mercury may be 100 per cent carbon dioxide.

Since Mercury is so close to the Sun, has a low albedo, and was thought to have its sunlit side bathed in continual sunshine, scientists believed that the surface temperature on the sunlit side must be extremely high. Infrared observations suggest a value of 800° F. It was also believed that on the dark side the surface temperature would be extremely low. The reasoning went this way: Since the "back" side never saw the Sun, and since the tiny amount of atmosphere was not capable of transporting heat from sunlit side to dark side, the dark side of Mercury must be frigid. Theoretical estimates of the temperature on the dark side had run as low as –246° C. (–410° F.), which is within about 27° C. (49° F.) of the absolute zero of temperature. But the new radar observations, combined with a re-analysis of the previous telescopic observations and theoretical work, indicate that the planet's rotation period is not equal to its orbital period. The "back" side does indeed see the Sun. The new rotation period—59 days—is, however, quite long, and the night side of the planet (if this figure is correct) must be in darkness for many days. Since little atmosphere exists to transport heat from sunlit side to dark side, one would still expect very low temperatures on the dark side. Recent microwave observations, however, have spoiled this picture of a frozen world on the dark side of Mercury. These microwave readings indicate that the dark side is much warmer than believed; surface temperatures are not as low as those predicted and may even be as high as about 60° F. But how does one explain such relatively warm temperatures? Small as it is, the atmosphere may transfer some of the heat from the broiling sunlit side to the night side.

Jupiter

Beyond the orbit of Mars are the four giants of the solar system. Jupiter, named for the chief of the gods of the ancient Romans, is by far the largest of all. All the other planets could be placed inside this giant without crowding. To the telescope, Jupiter presents a slightly yellowish face crossed by dark and light bands that are parallel to its equator (Plate VII). The dark bands are called belts, the light ones zones. On close inspection, the belts reveal much detail, with darker and lighter portions, spots, and irregular fine structure. Some of these features last for many weeks, and it is a simple matter to determine the rotation rate from observations of the reappearance of these long-lasting features. Other features are short-lived. The variability of the observed features suggests that when we observe Jupiter we see not its surface but cloud bands in its atmosphere. Like Venus, Jupiter is keeping its surface secrets to itself.

Since Jupiter has a high escape velocity, we infer that it retains some lighter gases, such as hydrogen and helium (the two lightest), in its atmosphere. Spectroscopic observations have confirmed the presence of hydrogen and given some indication of the amount above Jupiter's cloud top. Helium in a planet's atmosphere, on the other hand, is difficult to detect spectroscopically. Its presence in Jupiter's atmosphere is deduced in the following argument. The total amount of atmosphere above Jupiter's cloud top can be deduced from the pressure at the cloud top. This pressure recently has been estimated. The measured amount of hydrogen is not sufficient to account for the total amount of atmosphere deduced from the cloud-top pressure; in fact, the amount of hydrogen is sufficient to account for only about 60 per cent of the total atmosphere. Thus, there must be other gases besides hydrogen in the atmosphere. Another important observation suggests that the mean molecular weight of Jupiter's atmosphere is between 3 and 4. The molecular weights of some common atmospheric gases are: hydrogen, 2; helium, 4; nitrogen, 28; oxygen, 32; carbon dioxide, 44. Now, the mean molecular weight of an atmosphere is an average of the molecular weights of the individual gases in the atmosphere. For Jupiter, then, we have the following information: hydrogen accounts for 60 per cent of the atmosphere, and the mean molecular weight is between 3 and 4. It is reasonable to infer that helium, with a molecular weight of 4, is the other major constituent of Jupiter's atmosphere. Direct observational confirmation of this deduction has yet to come.

Spectroscopic observations also indicate the presence of small amounts of methane and ammonia in the atmosphere. Since both gases contain hydrogen atoms, detection adds additional evidence for the presence of atmospheric hydrogen. What about nitrogen, which is the major constituent of our atmosphere and is thought to be the major constituent of the atmosphere of Venus? Any nitrogen that may have been in the atmosphere probably has combined with hydrogen to form ammonia. One recent estimate of the percentages of various gases in Jupiter's atmosphere is shown in Fig. 31. Jupiter's atmosphere is certainly much different from our own.

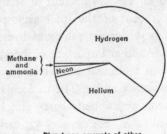

Fig. 31 Pie graph illustrating estimated composition of the atmosphere of Jupiter.

Based upon Jupiter's distance from the Sun and its albedo, theoretical estimates of the temperature indicate a value of −168° C. (−270° F.). The greenhouse effect of the planet's atmosphere should raise the surface temperature above this value. Measurements of temperature obtained from radiation observations refer not to Jupiter's surface but to levels near the cloud tops; the clouds and the rest of the atmosphere effectively screen the surface from our radiometers. These radiation measurements suggest a temperature of about −123° C. (−189° F.) near the cloud top. Undoubtedly, the temperatures are higher near the surface; how much higher, no one really knows.

The total amount of Jupiter's atmosphere is unknown. Scientists expect the total to be large because the high escape velocity would make it difficult for atmospheric molecules to fly off into outer space. The atmospheric pressure at the level of the cloud tops has been estimated recently to be about three times the surface pressure on Earth. In one theoretical model of Jupiter the surface atmospheric pressure is estimated to be 200,000 times the surface pressure on the Earth. Thus the planet itself lies at the bottom of a huge ocean of atmosphere. The surface of the planet, according to this theoretical model, may be composed of liquid hydrogen and may be at a temperature of close to 2000° C. (3632° F.). A steady flow of heat from the interior would be required to maintain such a high temperature, the heat coming from decay of radioactive elements. Conditions such as these remind us much more of the Sun than of the other planets we have discussed so far.

The spots and other markings in Jupiter's cloud bands give us a measure for determining winds at the cloud levels. The equatorial clouds consistently have an eastward speed that is about 100 meters per second (224 miles per hour) greater than the clouds at other latitudes. Thus, the equatorial atmosphere appears to spin more rapidly than the other parts of the planet do. The rotation period of the equatorial atmosphere is 9 hours 50 minutes, 5 minutes less than the rotation period of the atmosphere at other latitudes. The higher speed of the equatorial atmosphere is called the *equatorial acceleration*. Why it should occur, nobody is quite sure. It has been suggested that the equatorial acceleration on Jupiter is similar to the jet streams (narrow belts of strong winds blowing from west to east) of our own atmosphere. A somewhat similar phenomenon occurs on the Sun. It has been known for many years that the rotation rate of the Sun is not constant but changes with latitude; the Sun's rotation rate is greatest at its equator and decreases according to latitude. The explanation of the Sun's varying rotation rate is unknown.

The equatorial acceleration on Jupiter refers to the high speed of the cloud-top wind at the equator compared with the speed at other latitudes. Very recently, scientists have interpreted certain spectroscopic observations to mean that the equatorial clouds may move much faster than the atmosphere above them—as much as 4000 to 6000 meters per second (9000 to 13,000 miles per hour) faster at times. Now, a wind of 10,000 miles per hour is indeed fantastic. In our strongest tornadoes on Earth, the winds never exceed 200 to 300 miles per hour. If these observations are confirmed, the explanation of such a fantastic wind will put a great strain on the meteorologist.

Some scientists interpret the light bands and spots as cloud-filled storms, and the dark bands and spots as regions of good weather. Both light and dark spots move generally from west to east, the prevailing direction of storm movement in our own atmosphere.

Although the duration of most spots in Jupiter's atmosphere is a matter of only hours, days, or weeks, there is one large spot that has been in view for at least 130 years.* This is Jupiter's famous Great Red Spot (Plate VII). The Great Red Spot is oval-shaped and is about 22,000 miles long and 7000 miles wide; its surface area is almost equal to the Earth's. Over the years, it has undergone changes in color and brightness as well as in form and size. It has shifted position—as much as 20,000 miles from its average position—although its movements seem to be confined to an east-west direction. Thus, although its longitude has changed over the years, its latitude has remained more or less constant.

There are currently two different theories to explain this apparently permanent feature of the planet. One theory suggests that the Red Spot is a large solid body floating in Jupiter's thick atmosphere. There are problems with this hypothesis, including the difficulty of finding a suitable solid ma-

* The German amateur astronomer S. H. Schwabe drew the Red Spot in 1831. A suggestion of its appearance has been found in a sketch made in 1664 by the brilliant English scientist Robert Hooke.

terial that might float in Jupiter's atmosphere. The other theory suggests that a shallow but extensive mountain on the surface of the planet causes the spot. The shallow mountain, so the argument goes, disrupts the motion of the air over it. This disruption extends into the higher atmosphere, where it affects the appearance of the clouds. The clouds high above the shallow mountain then look different from other cloud areas. It is this different cloud formation that we call the Red Spot. But how does this theory explain the movements of the Red Spot? Perhaps the solid surface of the planet does not rotate uniformly—that is, some areas of the planet may rotate faster than other areas—and the Red Spot is only following the movement of the shallow mountain. This is a rather difficult picture to imagine. A mountain that moves about and has a Great Red Spot the size of the Earth faithfully following it? But this theory is apparently the leading contender for the explanation of Jupiter's Great Red Spot.

It is the general belief that ammonia crystals compose Jupiter's visible clouds. This belief is based upon the observed presence of ammonia gas in the atmosphere and temperatures of the cloud top. At the cloud top the temperature is about −123° C. (−189° F.). Ammonia freezes at −78° C. (−108° F.). Thus, the topmost parts of the cloud could be made of frozen ammonia crystals. There is the possibility of clouds made of liquid droplets of ammonia lower down in the warmer part of the atmosphere. Such a situation would be similar to that prevailing in our own atmosphere, where we have ice crystal clouds in the upper layers and water droplet clouds in the lower layers. It has also been suggested that water clouds—both the ice crystal and water droplet variety—are present deep down in Jupiter's atmosphere.

In summary, we may say that Jupiter resembles the Sun almost as much as it resembles the Earth. Its size is intermediate between Earth and Sun; its atmospheric composition of hydrogen and helium is similar to the Sun's atmosphere. Its equatorial acceleration resembles a similar phenomenon on the Sun. Jupiter may not receive all its heat from the distant Sun; it may generate some internally. The outstanding puzzles are: (1) the Great Red Spot, (2) the equatorial acceleration, and (3) conditions below the cloud layer. Instrumented spacecraft sent toward Jupiter may help solve these puzzles.

Saturn

The view we get of Saturn through a telescope is breathtaking. Saturn is probably the most beautiful object in the sky. Anyone at all interested in astronomy knows Saturn as the planet with the spectacular rings around it (Plate VIII). The planet itself is yellowish in color, but not as bright as Jupiter. Bands, not very pronounced, cross Saturn parallel to the equator. Occasionally white spots appear, but, the rings apart, there is no outstanding permanent feature to compare with Jupiter's Great Red Spot. The color, the high albedo, and the impermanence of observable features indicate the presence of a cloud layer. The planet appears to be a quieter version of its neighbor Jupiter.

Spectroscopic searches have identified several gases—methane, ammonia, and hydrogen—in Saturn's atmosphere. There is more methane and hydrogen, and less ammonia, than in Jupiter's atmosphere. Helium, though undetectable from Earth, is believed generally to be the other major constituent. Thus, Saturn's atmosphere appears to be quite similar to Jupiter's—large quantities of hydrogen and helium, with a dash of methane and ammonia.

Theoretical estimates of Saturn's surface temperature, based upon its distance from the Sun but not on a possible greenhouse effect, yield a value of −195° C. (−319° F.). Infrared and microwave observations suggest a temperature of about −167° C. (−269° F.). The observed temperatures are believed, however, to refer to the atmosphere near the cloud tops rather than to the surface. The temperature at the surface has not been measured. One recent theory suggests that the surface temperature of both Saturn and Jupiter runs about 2000° C. (3632° F.). According to this theory, the heat required to keep the surface at such high temperature comes from within the planet and is the result of radioactive decay. It is interesting to note that over the past fifty years the theorists have gone from hot to cold and now back to hot again in their estimates of temperature on the surfaces of Jupiter and Saturn. To settle the matter once and for all, we need a good measurement with instruments and in all likelihood we'll not obtain it until we launch planetary probes to these planets.

It is believed that Saturn has a large amount of atmosphere. Estimates of the pressure at the visible surface—that is, the cloud tops—range from 0.3 to 3 times the surface pressure on Earth. The recent hot-surface theory for Saturn and Jupiter calls for surface pressures of about 200,000 times Earth's surface pressure of 1000 millibars. The cloud tops, in these theoretical models, would be at a height of nearly 5000 miles above the surface.

The winds in Saturn's atmosphere appear to be similar to the winds in Jupiter's atmosphere. The atmosphere above the equatorial region rotates more rapidly than the atmosphere over other parts of the planet. In fact, the atmosphere over the equator completes one rotation around the axis of the planet in 25 minutes less than the atmosphere at 60° latitude. The cause of these higher equatorial wind velocities is not known.

The clouds in the atmosphere of Saturn are believed to be composed of frozen ammonia crystals, as on Jupiter. There is also the possibility of a thin cloud layer of methane high above the main ammonia cloud layer, and of ice crystal and water droplet clouds below it. If this is so, a weather forecaster on Saturn would have not only the problem of forecasting the amount of cloudiness, but also the type of clouds—methane, ammonia, or water. Fig. 32 ties together some of the discussion of Saturn and Jupiter in the form of a graphical representation of their atmospheres. It should be remembered that there

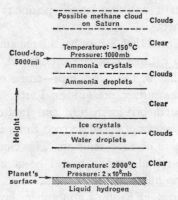

Fig. 32 A problem for weather forecasters—a chart of possible cloud layers in the atmospheres of Jupiter and Saturn.

are still many uncertainties, and this picture is subject to change as better observations are made.

Before moving on to Uranus, we should say something about Saturn's rings, although they are really not part of the planet's atmosphere. There are actually three rings surrounding the planet (Fig. 33),

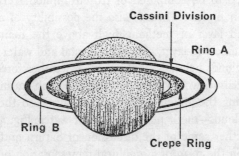

Fig. 33 The rings of Saturn. (After Patrick Moore.)

if the planet has taken a tumble and is flat on its back. As a result of this peculiar inclination, the seasons on Uranus are strange. Fig. 34 shows Uranus at four different times in its orbit around the Sun.

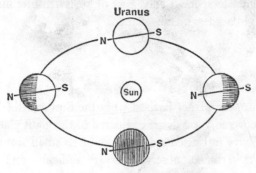

Fig. 34   *The unusual inclination of Uranus keeps half of the planet in complete darkness through the period when one pole faces the Sun. Poles are indicated by N and S.*

In one position Uranus' north pole faces the Sun and represents the subsolar point; in the opposite position Uranus' south pole faces the Sun and represents the subsolar point. During the seasons represented by both these positions only one hemisphere receives solar radiation, the other hemisphere being in darkness. We would expect the temperature in these seasons to be a maximum at one pole and to decrease to a minimum at the other pole. In the other two positions shown in Fig. 34, Uranus' equator faces the Sun, and, as the planet rotates about its axis, the entire planet receives solar radiation. These positions are quite similar to spring and fall

on the Earth, and we would expect the temperature
to be a maximum at the equator and to decrease
poleward. Since the seasons are quite long, about 21
years each, it would be entirely possible, in a polar
region, to spend a good part of an Earth lifetime in
total darkness on this planet.

Pluto

Pluto, the planet farthest from the Sun and the last
discovered,* is a dwarf compared to the giant planets
we have just discussed. Because of its small size and
great distance, observations are difficult, and we
know very little about it. Through the telescope it
appears yellowish-whitish. Variations in surface
brightness are extremely difficult to make out, even
with the largest telescopes. Spectroscopic observations have not even been attempted. At such a great
distance from the Sun, the planet receives extremely
little solar radiation, and the probable average surface temperature is put at about −212° C. (−350°
F.). At such low temperatures, most common atmospheric gases would be condensed into their
liquid or solid form. Hydrogen and helium would
still be gaseous, but since Pluto's escape velocity is
probably low, these light gases most likely have escaped. Thus, our knowledge of the composition of
Pluto's atmosphere is uncertain, to say the least. The

* Pluto was discovered in 1930 by Clyde W. Tombaugh,
an American astronomer.

low albedo of the planet suggests that the atmosphere may be cloudless. Because of the large eccentricity of the orbit, we would expect the average temperature to vary by as much as 25 per cent between the positions nearest to and farthest from the Sun. But the temperature must be so low to begin with that a 25 per cent variation should not cause much change.

The large eccentricity also takes Pluto occasionally within the orbit of Neptune. For example, between the years 1969 and 2009 Pluto will be within the orbit of Neptune and will actually be closer to the Earth and Sun than Neptune is. During this time Pluto will relinquish its distinction as the far-out planet. The relatively long rotation period of over six days gives the planet nights lasting more than 72 hours. Another interesting feature is the long time it takes to complete one revolution around the Sun—248 years. Thus, each season lasts about 62 years, or approximately the lifetime of a human being. Since the planet receives so little heat from the Sun, there is no process of energy distribution to create strong winds. Whatever winds blow on Pluto are probably gentle. All in all, the far-out planet appears to be a quiet, frozen world.

Two Families of Planets

The giant planets—Jupiter, Saturn, Uranus, and Neptune—are so different from the others that scientists divide the solar system into two families. One family consists of the giant planets, the other of the terrestrial planets—Mercury, Earth, Venus, Mars, and Pluto. The giants have many features in common. They are all large, rotate rapidly, and have thick atmospheres of hydrogen, helium, ammonia, and methane. There is the possibility that they have large internal heat sources. Their equatorial regions seem to spin faster than the regions at higher latitude. In all these characteristics, except the one of fast rotation, the giant planets are similar to the Sun. (The Sun's rotation period of 27 days is much longer than the rotation periods of the giant planets.) These characteristics are certainly different from those of the terrestrial planets. The terrestrial planets are small, rotate relatively slowly, have thin atmospheres (although Venus may be an exception), and lack large internal heat sources and equatorial accelerations. Their atmospheres have no hydrogen, helium, methane, or ammonia.

The terrestrial planets differ quite considerably among themselves. First, there is little Mercury, with its tiny atmosphere that may be entirely composed of carbon dioxide. Then comes Venus with its perpetual cloud cover, its high surface temperature, long days and nights, and an atmosphere of nitrogen and carbon dioxide. Beyond Venus is our home—the Earth—the only planet with oxygen in its atmosphere. Beyond us lies the red planet, Mars, with its mysterious color changes, large daily temperature variations, icecaps, and clouds of different color. And then, out beyond the four giant planets, in the far reaches of the solar system, moves the last of the terrestrial planets, Pluto, quiet and frozen.

Chapter VII

WHAT NEXT?

As you must realize by now, there are many things we do not know about the atmospheres of the planets. Some of the things we do know have confronted us with puzzles. What are the major unanswered questions, and what plans have we to find the answers?

Unsolved Puzzles

The observations indicate that the temperature at the surface of Venus is remarkably high—about 800° F. But according to our Earthbound way of looking at things Venus should have a surface temperature not much warmer than ours. Why is it so hot on Venus? Do the thick atmosphere and cloud layer magnify the expected greenhouse effect and so keep the surface hot? Do constant winds sweeping the planet with dust and sand heat the surface by friction? Or is there some other mechanism that we have not yet thought of that can be heating the surface? No one really knows.

Every Martian spring the thin polar icecap melts

away, and a "wave of darkening" spreads along the planet's surface from the shrinking cap. It moves toward the equatorial regions, by way of the dark areas, at a speed of about 20 miles per day. What is this "wave of darkening" on Mars? Has it something to do with the release of moisture into the dry atmosphere by the melting icecaps? Is some primitive form of vegetation responding to the increased moisture and going through a growth cycle? Are winds transporting moisture from one pole to the other? No one really knows.

It was believed for a long time that the rotation period of little Mercury, closest neighbor of the Sun, was equal to its period of revolution about the Sun. But, as we have seen, this belief has been shattered by recent observational and theoretical calculations. What other surprises may Mercury have in store for us? Has it really any atmosphere at all? Why is the night side, which doesn't see the Sun for many days at a stretch, so relatively warm? How important is a thin, vacuum-like atmosphere in the transport of heat from sunlit side to dark side? Again, no one knows for sure.

In the atmosphere of Jupiter's southern hemisphere there is a gigantic oval-shaped formation—the Great Red Spot—whose surface area is equal to the Earth's. Wandering freely back and forth in an east-west direction, the Great Red Spot manages to keep itself in the same latitude zone. Is the Great Red Spot a special kind of cloud? Is it caused by the disruption of the air motion over a moving, shallow mountain? Or is it some large body floating in Jupiter's dense atmosphere? Or is it something else?

The giant planets—Jupiter, Saturn, Uranus, and Neptune—all are large, rotate rapidly, have thick atmospheres of hydrogen, helium, ammonia, and methane, and may have internal heat sources and spin more rapidly at their equators. The terrestrial planets—Mercury, Venus, Earth, Mars, and Pluto— are small, rotate slowly, have thin atmospheres, but lack internal heat sources and significant amounts of hydrogen, helium, ammonia, and methane in their atmospheres, and do not spin faster at the equator. Why should there be these differences between two groups of planets in the same solar system? Are there other planets—not yet discovered— in our solar system?

These questions lead us to the most important questions of all. How did the solar system form? Is there some kind of life on any of the planets besides Earth? Again, we must say that no one really knows —but we may soon find out.

Voyager: Unmanned Landings on Mars and Venus

The expanding program of planetary observations from astronomical observatories, from balloon-borne telescopes, and from planetary fly-bys similar to the Mariner missions is constantly increasing our knowledge of the planets. But all these observations are indirect, for none of them actually has been within a planetary atmosphere itself; they all rely on the interpretation of a measurement of electromagnetic radiation. When will we place instruments directly within the atmospheres of the planets and at their surfaces? Scientists currently are designing an instrumented spacecraft that will explore our neighboring planets. The name of the spacecraft is Voyager; its first trip is scheduled for around 1973.

Voyager will be a 7000-pound unmanned spacecraft. Its primary purpose will be a scientific exploration of Mars and Venus, with emphasis on finding out whether some form of life exists or has existed on these planets. In addition, it will make scientific measurements in interplanetary space on the way to its destination. Voyager also will test whether it is practical to send manned flights to these planets and will collect scientific data that are necessary for the planning of manned flights.

Since we want to determine whether there is any form of life on Mars, we must be extremely careful not to contaminate the planet with our own Earthly germs carried along on the spacecraft. Therefore, the entire spacecraft must be sterilized before launch. This is not an easy matter. It is quite obvious, as one scientist has said, that sterilizing a spaceship with 19,000 parts will be more difficult than sterilizing a surgeon's instruments or a can of tomatoes.

Let us follow Voyager on a trip to Mars. Because of its great weight—ten times the weight of Mariner —Voyager will need a very powerful rocket to launch it. A rocket called Saturn, which also will launch our astronauts on their trip to the Moon, will power

Voyager. The timing will have to be perfect. The spacecraft will be able to reach Mars only when the planet is nearest the Earth, a period of one month coming about every two years (Fig. 35). If we are

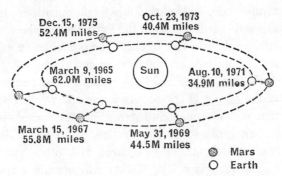

Fig. 35 *Mars and Earth are closest to each other once every two years or so. Diagram illustrates these times and the Earth–Mars distances, in millions of miles, at these times up to the year 1975. (After W. R. Corliss. Courtesy of International Science and Technology.)*

not ready on time, we shall have to wait two years for another try. On the way to Mars, Voyager will measure the numbers and kinds of particles and dusts that are found in interplanetary space. The part of the spacecraft that will make these measurements is called the interplanetary bus.

About one-half year after launch Voyager will arrive near Mars. At this stage, a landing vehicle (lander) will leave the spacecraft, descend through the Martian atmosphere, and settle on the surface. Meanwhile, Voyager will go into orbit around Mars, where it will be able to observe the planet from above and act as a radio transmitting station in communicating signals from the lander to Earth. As it descends on Mars the instrumented lander will measure directly temperature, pressure, atmospheric composition, and other atmospheric quantities—just as weather balloons do in the Earth's atmosphere. At last, we shall be able to check the estimates we have made from indirect observations and theory.

The lander will make observations on the surface of the planet (Fig. 36). An automatic weather station will measure temperature, pressure, wind, humidity, atmospheric composition, atmospheric dust content, amount of cloudiness, and other atmospheric quantities. The station will operate for six

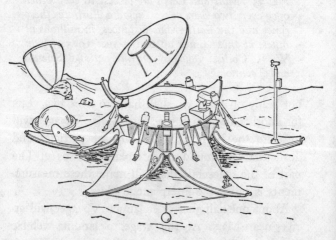

Fig. 36 An artist's conception of the Voyager lander on the surface of Mars. (Courtesy of AVCO Corporation.)

months, transmitting its data to Voyager, which will relay them to Earth.

Also aboard the lander will be instruments for analyzing the composition of the Martian surface and, most importantly, for detecting the presence of life on the surface. Although no specific program has been decided upon, several possible experiments would follow this line. Only small organisms, if any, are expected on Mars. The instruments will pick up a sample of Martian soil for analysis. In one experiment, the soil sample, after being "fed" a "soup" that will make organisms grow and reproduce rapidly, will be placed under a microscope attached to a television camera. Inspection of these transmitted pictures should reveal whether living organisms are present. Another experiment will seek evidence of photosynthesis, the process by which vegetable life on Earth combines sunlight and atmospheric carbon dioxide into food. Scientists think that photosynthesis, since it is so common on Earth, may be characteristic of life on Mars. In the photosynthesis experiment, a fixed amount of carbon dioxide will be made available to the soil sample in daytime and at night. If the soil sample uses up some of the carbon dioxide during the day but not at night then we will have good evidence that photosynthesis is taking place, and therefore, that there is some form of life on the planet. In this experiment, the quantity to be measured and radioed back to Earth will be the amount of carbon dioxide. In a third life detection experiment, the basic characteristic of animal life on Earth—that it gives off carbon dioxide—will be the crux. Any carbon dioxide given off by the soil sample would be evidence of life.

A television camera and a microphone may also be part of the lander. The television camera would scan the area around the landing site, while the microphone would pick up Martian noises. No one knows what sort of noises to expect. It would be a delightful surprise indeed if we should pick up the songs of Martian bird life.

While the lander will remain at one spot on the Martian surface, the Voyager will scout all Mars from a height of about 1000 miles as it orbits the planet. On board will be: a television camera for mapping the Martian surface and observing clouds, infrared and ultraviolet spectrometers for detecting gases in the atmosphere, and infrared and microwave radiometers for mapping the surface temperatures over the Martian globe.

TABLE 2

TENTATIVE TIMETABLE FOR SPACE EXPLORATION

Year	Tentative Timetable
1962	Unmanned Mariner spacecraft flies by Venus
1965	Unmanned Mariner spacecraft flies by Mars
1970	Man lands on the Moon
1973	Unmanned Voyager spacecraft lands on Mars
1985	Man lands on Mars

A tentative schedule for future space exploration is given in Table 2. If the results of the Voyager trips to Mars and Venus are in the least bit encouraging, there is no doubt that manned flights to these planets will take place. After successful completion of a manned trip to the Moon, Mars will become the number one target for space exploration. The timetable is short. Most of us will be around when the events happen.

APPENDIX

A Word About Numbers, Units, and Symbols

Any number can be written as the product of a number between 1 and 10 and a number which is a power of 10. For example, we can write 854 as 8.54×100; 62,500 as $6.25 \times 10,000$; and 3,200,000,000 as $3.2 \times 1,000,000,000$. There is a short way of writing such numbers. Instead of 100 we write 10^2; instead of 10,000 we write 10^4; and instead of 1,000,000,000 we write 10^9. Our numbers can now be written as:

$$854 = 8.54 \times 10^2$$
$$62,500 = 6.25 \times 10^4$$
$$3,200,000,000 = 3.2 \ \times 10^9$$

In this notation, $10^0 = 1$, $10^1 = 10$, $10^2 = 100$, $10^3 = 1000$, etc. Similarly with numbers less than 1. For example, the number 0.12 is $1.2 \times \frac{1}{10}$; 0.0023 is $2.3 \times \frac{1}{1000}$; 0.0000495 is $4.95 \times \frac{1}{100,000}$. In place of $\frac{1}{10}$, we can write 10^{-1}; instead of $\frac{1}{1000}$, which equals $\frac{1}{10^3}$, we can write 10^{-3}; and in place of $\frac{1}{100,000}$, which equals $\frac{1}{10^5}$, we can write 10^{-5}. Our numbers less than 1 can now be written as:

$$0.12 = 1.2 \ \times 10^{-1}$$
$$0.0023 = 2.3 \ \times 10^{-3}$$
$$0.0000495 = 4.95 \times 10^{-5}$$

In this notation, $10^{-1} = \frac{1}{10}$, $10^{-2} = \frac{1}{100}$, $10^{-3} = \frac{1}{1000}$,

etc. This way of writing numbers is especially useful
for extremely large or extremely small numbers.

Scientists generally use metric units for their measurements. Such units as meters for distance and degrees Celsius (or Centigrade) for temperature are
metric units. Most of us are more familiar with the
English units of inches, feet, or miles for distance,
and degrees Fahrenheit for temperature. The relationship between some metric and English units
for length and mass, and the abbreviations of these
units, are shown below.

Metric   *English*
1 centimeter (cm)   = 0.394 inches (in.)
1 meter (m)   = 10^2 cm   = 3.28 feet (ft.)
1 kilometer (km)   = 10^3 m   = 0.621 miles (mi.)
1 kilogram (kg)   = 10^3 g   = 2.2 pounds (lb.)
1 gram (g)   = 0.035 ounces (oz.)

Temperatures given in degrees Celsius (°C.) can
be changed to degrees Fahrenheit (°F.) by the
formula

$$F. = \frac{9}{5}C. + 32$$

where F. is the temperature in °F. and C. is the
temperature in °C. For example, 0° C. is equal to
32° F.

In this book we have used both metric and English
units. Where metric units are used, their approxi-
mate equivalents in English units are given in pa-
rentheses.

SUGGESTED ADDITIONAL
READING

ON ASTRONOMY

An Introduction to Astronomy by R. H. Baker, D. Van Nostrand Co., Princeton.

Splendor in the Sky by G. S. Hawkins, Harper and Row, New York.

ON TELESCOPES AND ASTRONOMICAL INSTRUMENTS

Tools of the Astronomer by G. R. Miczaika and W. M. Sinton, Harvard University Press, Cambridge, Mass.

ON THE SOLAR SYSTEM

The Planets by Patrick Moore, W. W. Norton & Company, New York.

Earth, Moon, and Planets by Fred L. Whipple, Harvard University Press, Cambridge, Mass.

The Planet Venus by Patrick Moore, Macmillan Company, New York.

A Guide to Mars by Patrick Moore, Macmillan Company, New York.

ON METEOROLOGY

The Challenge of the Atmosphere by O. G. Sutton, Harper and Brothers, New York.

The Restless Atmosphere by F. K. Hare, Harper Torchbooks, Harper and Row, New York.

THE SCIENCE STUDY SERIES

The Nature of Violent Storms by Louis J. Battan.

Radar Observes the Weather by Louis J. Battan.

Cloud Physics and Cloud Seeding by Louis J. Battan.

PERIODICALS

Sky and Telescope, Sky Publishing Corporation, Cambridge, Mass.

Weatherwise, American Meteorological Society, Boston.

INDEX

SCIENCE STUDY SERIES